East Anglia

Dovercourt.

CIVIL ENGINEERING HERITAGE

East Anglia

Peter Cross-Rudkin

PHILLIMORE

2010
Phillimore & Co. Ltd.
Andover, Hampshire, England

ISBN 978-1-86077-637-3

ALSO IN THE CIVIL ENGINEERING HERITAGE SERIES
(General Editor: Peter Cross-Rudkin)

West Midlands by Roger Cragg

Wales by Keith Thomas

CONTENTS

Britain has a heritage of civil engineering structures and works unrivalled anywhere else. The skills of past engineers are in evidence throughout the land in a fascinating variety of bridges, structures, utilities and lines of communication: the infrastructure of society.

The series *Civil Engineering Heritage* makes available information about these works to a wide public in order to broaden the interest and understanding of the reader in the immense range of expertise that features in our history. In recent years people have become more aware of the value of our heritage and our responsibility to keep the best examples for future generations. It is therefore hoped that these books will assist those seeking to advance the cause of conservation.

Much of the information in these books, particularly in the gazetteer sections, has been extracted from the records of civil engineering works prepared by the Institution of Civil Engineers Panel for Historical Engineering Works (PHEW). The works covered by these records have been selected for their technical interest, innovation, association with eminent engineers or contractors, rarity or visual attraction. The Institution's Archives have become the principal national repository for records of civil engineering and are now regarded as the leading authority on historical engineering works. They are widely consulted by heritage organisations, the business community and those involved in private research. The records may be consulted by the public for research purposes on application to the Institution's Archivist. The relevant Historical Engineering Work number is given, where one exists, for each item in the gazetteer to assist researchers in following up items of interest. Additionally, PHEW has a number of subpanels dealing with specific types of civil engineering works in greater detail, who are able to assist with information about works within their remit.

The author would like to thank Peter Brown, who helped to tease out some of the trickier aspects of the Norfolk items, and Andrew Fakes, who supplied detailed information about Great Yarmouth at short notice. He is also grateful to the following members of PHEW for assistance with the preparation of this volume: Ian Anderson, the late Paul Dunkerley and Barry Barton; also Roger Cragg and Keith Thomas, authors of two other books in this series, who read the draft text and provided useful advice. As usual, the staff of the Archives and Library of the Institution of Civil Engineers responded to requests for information cheerfully and efficiently. Thanks are also due to the record offices at Cambridge, Chelmsford, Ipswich and Norwich, as well as the numerous other record offices, local authorities, public utilities and individuals, too numerous to mention, who have helped PHEW with their enquiries over the years.

Over the last 300 years, British civil engineers have been prominent in providing the infrastructure which has transformed the lives of the population not only of this country but throughout the world. In particular they have been noteworthy in the provision of transport facilities with the development of roads, inland waterways, railways, docks and harbours and, more recently, airports; in the provision of water supply, drainage and sewage treatment, and the provision of power supply for homes and industry from water, wind and fossil fuels. This book describes some of these works in East Anglia bequeathed to us by previous generations of civil engineers.

For the purpose of this book, East Anglia is taken to include the four post-1974 counties of Cambridgeshire, Essex, Norfolk and Suffolk, which with minor modifications include the ancient county of Huntingdonshire and the Soke of Peterborough, while excluding those parts of old Essex lost to Greater London.

The first five chapters of the book cover transport, bridges and tunnels, maritime, public utilities and power, and miscellaneous items. Sites printed in **bold** characters in these chapters can be found in the gazetteer, which is the second section of the book. This contains details of 95 sites arranged by county by county, all of which can be visited or seen from nearby. The national grid reference is given for each site and, where the location is not obvious from the description, information is given on access to the site.

The civil engineers who contributed to the development of East Anglia included many of the leading names of their day, including Sir Cornelius Vermuyden, John Rennie, Thomas Telford, Robert Stephenson and Sir John Hawkshaw. Local engineers, some of whom gained prominence outside the region, included Sir William Cubitt, Peter Bruff, George Edwards, William Thorold, John Valentine, Sir Morton Peto and the Lucas brothers. No attempt has been made here to describe all of their works – readers are referred to the two volumes of the *Biographical Dictionary of Civil Engineers of Great Britain and Ireland* for that – but it is hoped that enough is given to appreciate their contribution to the area.

East Anglia has generally been less heavily industrialised than some other parts of the United Kingdom, and the need for major civil engineering works has therefore been correspondingly smaller. Although there are few 'firsts' or 'the biggests' in the region, there is a wide variety of civil engineering heritage to see. Probably the two aspects that differentiate the region from most others are its fen drainage and sea defences. It is hoped that this book will encourage readers to seek out that heritage and understand more of why and how it came to be built.

Peter Cross-Rudkin
Castor, December 2009

Imperial measurements have been generally adopted for the dimensions of the works described in this book as this would have been the system used at the time of the design and construction of most of them. Where modern structures have been included which were designed and built using the metric system, metric units have been used in the text.

The following are the metric equivalents of the imperial units used:

Length:
1 inch = 25.4 millimetres
1 foot = 0.3048 metres
1 yard = 0.9144 metres
1 mile = 1.609 kilometres

Area:
1 square inch = 45.2 square millimetres
1 square foot = .0929 square metres
1 acre = 0.4047 hectares
1 square mile = 259 hectares

Volume:
1 gallon = 4.546 litres
1 million gallons = 4546 cubic metres
1 cubic yard = 0.7646 cubic metres

Mass:
1 pound = 0.4536 kilograms
1 ton = 1.016 tonnes

Power:
1 horsepower (h.p.) = 0.7457 kilowatts

Pressure:
1 pound force per square inch = 0.06895 bar

T he provision of transport infrastructure was one of the earlier benefits offered by civil engineering. Roads, navigable waterways, railways and, more recently, airports have provided the basis for much of commerce and leisure.

ROADS

Roman settlement in East Anglia was relatively dense, and a network of roads was created to serve it. The principal road connected London with the important Roman town of Colchester and continued north to Caistor St Edmund, the predecessor of Norwich. The modern A12 follows its alignment for many miles. Another main road left this route at Chelmsford to go via Long Melford before turning north-west in a direct line to the Wash at Holme next the Sea and a probable ferry across to Lincolnshire. The last leg of this road, known for the last 400 years or so as Peddar's Way, was probably built shortly after the suppression of Boudicca's revolt in A.D. 61 and is of more substantial construction than any other in East Anglia. A length of seven miles north of its crossing of the river Little Ouse (TL 9484) has more or less continuous remains of its agger, or embankment, and there are significant lengths elsewhere. At Hockham Heath (TL 9292) it turns slightly more to the north-west and continues closely on this alignment for no less than 34 miles to the coast. It has been a National Trail since 1986 and there is an extensive selection of guides and maps for those who wish to follow it.

Via Devana is another Roman road that acquired its name long after its builders had left the country — in this case only since the 18th century, when it was thought that it might be a route to Chester (Roman *Deva*). It probably started in Colchester but there is no trace of it until Sible Hedingham is reached, after which it goes via Haverhill to Cambridge. The section between Horseheath (TL 614477) and a modern road to Fulbourn (TL 489548) is followed by parish boundaries all the way and on the ground is marked by almost continuous agger, up to three feet high. Via Devana then bears west along the modern road called Worts Causeway, which is unusual in having been improved at least twice. The alignment of the Roman road here makes it clear that it took over a pre-existing track, and the name Worts commemorates Sir William Worts, who left money for its improvement when he died in 1709. The Roman road continues to the bridge over the river Cam that gave the town its name and then on to Godmanchester, where it joins Ermine Street.

An even more remarkable route is that known now as Fen Causeway. It connected the Roman town of *Durobrivae*, just outside Peterborough, with Denver in Norfolk. In the west it was a bank of gravel over fen ground, connecting the islands of Northey, Whittlesey and Eastrea. From there it continued as a canal to March, Nordelph and Upwell, in places with alternative channels. Later, as the canal silted up, a road was constructed along the bank of the canal. About 24 miles long, over difficult ground, parts of Fen Causeway are still marked on Ordnance Survey maps.

Unlike Roman roads, medieval highways were often no more than strip of land along a customary route, and by the Statute of Winchester of 1285 travellers had the right to go onto adjoining fields where the highway was impassable. In places, though, it was necessary to undertake some form of construction if a route was to be passable at all seasons. This was particularly true where marshy land was crossed. Three of the earliest medieval roads of which records exist are the causeways that led through the fens to the higher ground around Ely (**C16**). The causeways towards Stuntney and Aldreth were mentioned in the early 12th century, Haddenham from the 14th century.

Slightly later than medieval, but out of the ordinary line of development was Ireton's Way, between Ely and Chatteris (now the A142, although modern improvements have altered the line past Mepal). No road existed here before the Civil War, so it was constructed by the Parliamentary Major-General Ireton, allowing him to move his troops quickly to defend East Anglia as the need arose.

As roads became more defined, it was necessary to maintain them to keep the passage open. By an Act of 1555 each parish was made responsible for the roads within the parish. The work was to be supervised by elected highway surveyors and carried out by the parishioners themselves on appointed days under a system known as statute labour. With slight modification, this obligation endured until 1835, despite soon proving to be inadequate. A particular problem occurred where a long-distance route passed through a small parish that had no interest in maintaining the road for the benefit of others, nor the resources to do so. In 1609 and again in 1621 bills were presented to Parliament to permit tolls to be taken from travellers on the Great North Road in Hertfordshire to supplement the statute labour, but these were defeated. In 1663, however, petitions from some parishes on the Old North Road in Hertfordshire, Cambridgeshire and Huntingdonshire were successful in obtaining the first Turnpike Act, permitting toll gates to be set up at Wadesmill, Caxton and Stilton. Only that at Wadesmill seems to have been erected. Despite several attempts no further Act was passed until 1695, when ones for the Shenfield-Harwich road in Essex and Wymondham-Attleborough in Norfolk were obtained. This last took over a causeway that had been constructed 20 years earlier past Wymondham Mere. In 1698 the inveterate traveller Celia Fiennes rode on this causeway, 'for all about is not to be rode on unless it's a very dry summer'.

These early Acts gave the powers to the justices of the peace, adding another obligation to their already significant administrative duties. In 1706 the first Acts setting up turnpike trusts came into force, in Bedfordshire, Buckinghamshire, Wiltshire and Somerset. East Anglia had to wait until 1710 for a trust, not surprisingly to deal with the Royston-Wansford Bridge section of the Old North Road. The next trust in the region was set up in 1724, for the Newmarket-Chesterford section of the present A11, and the following year for the Trumpington-Foulmire (Fowlmere) section of the old route from Cambridge to London. 1729 saw a trust for roads around Wisbech and March and 1745 the Godmanchester-Newmarket Heath trust. The year 1751 saw the start of a turnpike mania, which would continue until 1772. During this period 389 new trusts were created, more than in all the years before or those after. East Anglia was relatively slow in entering this enthusiasm. There were no trusts established there between 1745 and 1755, when three were started in Huntingdonshire. Of the 389 trusts mentioned above, only 12 were wholly or partly in East Anglia.

Like their predecessors, the parish surveyors, the trustees of these early turnpikes were almost entirely concerned with the quality of the road surface. They could augment their income from tolls by the continuing use of statute labour, although this was still required for the maintenance of other roads in the parish as well. The results of their efforts were very variable. Much depended on the availability of suitable material to dress the surface at a reasonable cost. The flints found in parts of East Anglia did not combine well to provide a stable road, and in other parts where no stone was immediately available, the cost of transporting heavy loads was prohibitive.

In the 18th century, although surveyors were paid servants of the trust and had continuity of employment, and so might gain knowledge by experience, it was generally not a full-time occupation and few were professionals. A list in 1819 of the previous surveyors of six trusts included a Lloyd's Coffee House underwriter, many 'old, infirm men', a carpenter, a coal merchant, a baker and a publican. In 1810 it had been asserted that 'Surveyors are elected because they can measure; they might as well be elected because they can sing; but they are more commonly elected because they want a situation.' But by then this was no longer entirely true. In the 1790s John Hare of Kimberley was sufficiently well regarded to be the Surveyor of at least six trusts in Norfolk and Suffolk.

The best known of these new professionals was John Loudon McAdam. He became interested as a road trustee in his native Ayrshire in 1785. Having moved to Cornwall in 1798 and then to Bristol in 1802, and, after giving evidence to a select committee of the House of Commons in 1811, he was appointed surveyor of the Bristol Roads Turnpike Trust in 1816. By this time there were more than 800 trusts in existence and 110 years of experience, and not all bad. He reckoned that in his first 15 years in England he had travelled 30,000 miles at his own expense, collecting information about road making and administration, and on that basis he proposed 'to do what never yet has been done, to consider the making of the form and surface of roads scientifically'. This claim was not strictly correct, as similar ideas to his own had been proposed at least 70 years earlier, and Pierre Tresaguet in France had proposed a form of construction that engineers like Thomas Telford, Benjamin Wingrove and James Paterson were already putting into practice in Britain. McAdam's road construction was less solid than theirs and therefore cheaper, but adequate to the needs of most of the traffic of his time. His impact was just as important, though, in stressing the need for proper administration, and the consolidation of trusts in order to be able to afford to employ competent professionals.

In order to spread the uptake of his ideas, McAdam trained several members of his extended family and then obtained their election as Surveyors to a number of trusts. The Surveyor would retain overall responsibility but employ an assistant who would act on a day-to-day basis. In order to maintain an adequate level of contact, each member of the family concentrated on one or two areas. McAdam's second son, James, had a group in East Anglia; in 1818 he managed the Wadesmill, Kneesworth-Caxton and Huntingdon-Somersham trusts; in 1821 he added the Bury St Edmunds-Sudbury and Watton roads; in 1823 the Lynn Districts, Newmarket Heath and the north-west division of the Cambridge & Ely. He was a capable and tireless administrator and went on to be Surveyor of the Metropolis Roads in 1826, responsible for all the turnpike roads in London north of the River Thames, and was knighted in 1834.

Although by no means a universal phenomenon, other examples of multiple appointments could be found in many parts of the country. By 1839, J.H. Maher was surveyor of four trusts in Norfolk and one in Lincolnshire, earning £325 a year, and G.T. Knott of Eye was employed by nine trusts in Norfolk and Suffolk. The latter left at least two memorials of his work. The bridge on the old main road leading from Ipswich into Stowmarket is inscribed 'This bridge widened 13 foot 1842 Garrett Taylor Knott Surveyor', and a stone in the wall opposite the church at Cringleford, on the main road leading out of Norwich to London, records 'This road was widened 13 feet/ Anno Domini 1825/ Garrett Taylor Knott/ Surveyor'. Whether there was some special significance in the number 13 is not clear, but as the road in Cringleford was on a hill and an S-bend, and a second plaque records a further widening by 18ft in 1929, it must have been very tricky to negotiate before Knott set to work.

Only in their later days did turnpike trusts start to consider more than short lengths of new construction. The Chatteris Ferry-Downham Bridge trust in 1729 had constructed its route from Wisbech to March along the top of the five-mile long Waldersea Bank, the embankment that contained the River Nene and protected the lands below it to the east. In 1817, as part of a scheme for poor relief in the depression following the end of the Napoleonic Wars, the bank, then less than 30ft wide, was increased by 20ft and the road was gravelled. In 1810 the Cambridge & Ely Trust, whose area spread well beyond the two cities of its title, obtained an Act for a new road from Wisbech to Thorney, where it joined an existing turnpike road to Peterborough and provided an alternative route to the navigation described below. As there were then no bridges over the outfalls of the Ouse, Nene or Welland, this was the first all-year route from north Norfolk to the Midlands that did not depend on a ferry. On the other side of Norfolk, the construction of the **Acle New Road (N1)** in 1830-1 opened up an extensive tract of land that previously was almost completely isolated from the road system, as well as cutting five miles off the journey from Norwich to Great Yarmouth. In April 1830 (Sir) James McAdam was elected surveyor of the Epping & Ongar Trust and within two months had recommended a new line of road from Epping to Woodford Wells. It was constructed in 1833 by Bough & Smith and William Walker and is still known as the Epping New Road. McAdam was also the surveyor in 1824 of a new road from Littleport to Welney Ferry, where a suspension bridge was about to be constructed over the River Ouse, though in that case only 1,800 yards beside the river and a short length in Littleport were completely new. As late as 1839 a new road, part of what is now the B1387 south of Blythburgh, was authorised by Act of Parliament.

Sometimes roadside structures give clues to changes that have taken place. The importance of the present A11 road from Norwich towards London is attested by the pillar set up at Besthorpe in 1675 to commemorate the construction of the causeway past Wymondham Mere. The 16 milestones on the A10/B1368 between Trumpington and Barkway were set up in 1725-7 by a Fellow of Trinity Hall, Cambridge, on what was then a main route towards London. Most were replaced by larger stones in 1728-32 and are distinguished by the arms of Trinity Hall. The last four, in Hertfordshire, bear a cast-iron plate put up by the Wadesmill Turnpike Trust, who later took over the road. Before 1821 the traveller from Wisbech to King's Lynn would use the present route as far as Terrington St John, then continue south-east to Lordsbridge before deciding whether to continue straight on to cross the river at Wiggenhall St Mary Magdalen or turn north to Wiggenhall St German. Then the great loop in the River Ouse at Eau Brink was straightened and the river immediately upstream of King's Lynn narrowed.

1 *(Far left) Trinity Hall milestone, Cambridge-Foulmire road.*

2 *Magdalen Tollhouse, Wiggenhall St Mary Magdalen.*

3 *Sicklesmere Tollhouse.*

4   *Alconbury Hill guidepost.*

5   *Soham steelyard.*

As part of that project, the first Marshland Free Bridge was built and in 1823 diversion of the turnpike road to its route through Tilney High End required two long straight stretches of road (later the A47) to be built. The tollhouses at Lordsbridge (TF 571124) and Magdalen (TF 596117) still survive well away from any present main roads. This latter is of a standard type on turnpike roads around King's Lynn; another at Clenchwarton (TF 579203) halves the angle between the turnpike roads to Cross Keys and Wisbech. There could be interesting variations on a standard theme: the tollhouse at Sicklesmere (TL 877607) on the 1762 turnpike from Bury St Edmunds to Sudbury has two storeys but the one at Botesdale (TM 052763) between Bury and Scole, seven years later, is single-storey.

Another 'stray' is the direction post at Alconbury Hill in Huntingdonshire that gives distances to London by the old and the new North Roads, through Royston or Baldock. It is now at TL 187783, half a mile north of its original position at the junction of A14 and the A1; when it was erected the A1 going south turned right from it.

Alconbury Hill was also the scene from 1957 of an experiment to determine whether or not current design methods for highway pavements gave acceptable results. The road was being rebuilt in order to provide dual carriageways, so two trial lengths were constructed, one with flexible construction and the other with rigid, with about 30 short lengths of each, with varying depths and compositions. Performance of the different sections was monitored over six years, at the end of which it was found that the design methods were slightly conservative. In the meantime, however, the first length of motorway in Britain, the M6 Preston bypass, had opened and failed in use, so the design manual was kept as it was to allow a reasonable factor of safety. The A1 at Alconbury Hill was converted to motorway in 1998 and the 18th-century direction post mentioned above was taken from the central reservation and once again placed beside the road, where it can be inspected in peace now in the verge of the B1043.

Another item of roadside furniture that bears witness to road construction in the past is the weighing machine. Much of the 18th-century legislation to do with roads was concerned more with defining the width of the wheels of vehicles, the number of horses that might be allowed or limiting the weight that wagons might carry than with making the road sufficiently strong to bear the traffic. By an Act of 1741 turnpike trusts were permitted to erect weighing machines and charge £1 for every hundredweight over the legal maximum of three tons. Only two such steelyards remain *in situ* in the country, both in East Anglia, in Fountain Lane, Soham and New Street, Woodbridge.

The turnpike road system developed in a haphazard fashion. There were nine turnpike roads radiating from Norwich, each controlled by a separate trust. Five roads east of King's

Lynn were turnpiked in 1770 but for two trusts only. Essex was the scene of several of the early Acts for turnpikes, but many of the roads in the county were absorbed into the Essex Trust, which for administrative purposes was organised into several divisions. It was one of the most successful financially, becoming almost entirely free of debt. At its peak in East Anglia the system displayed some interesting gaps. There were no turnpikes to Hadleigh in Suffolk, an ancient and sizeable market town. In Norfolk, although the roads from King's Lynn to Narborough and Norwich to Swaffham were turnpiked, there was a gap from Narborough to Swaffham on what is now the A47. The northern route via Fakenham was only undertaken after two Acts of 1823 and 1828 for the eastern and western halves respectively. North of this route (now the A1067/A148), there were branches to Dersingham, Wells and Cromer, but none along the coast, even though it was a coach route.

The 20th century has seen the upgrading of roads to deal with increased and heavier traffic, though East Anglia has benefited (or suffered, according to one's point of view) rather less than other parts of the country. The Colchester bypass was built in 1930-3, three-quarters funded by central government to provide work for the unemployed. The M11 is the only motorway in East Anglia, though dual carriageway roads with grade-separated junctions exist on parts of the A11, A12 and A14 (formerly A45). The A12 improvements used crushed concrete from airfields redundant after the Second World War, an early example of recycling.

NAVIGATIONS

East Anglia benefited from early times from having an extensive network of navigable rivers. A few rivers were improved by cutting off bends and providing locks, but almost without exception the wholly artificial navigations were extensions to or branches off existing navigable rivers.

The most extensive system of river navigations was that based on the river Great Ouse. The improvements to the river itself over the centuries have been driven by the need for drainage, sometimes to the detriment of navigation and often opposed by boat owners and merchants. These developments are described in Chapter 5. The first navigation works on the Ouse itself were made under a patent granted in 1617, and the river was navigable up to Bedford by 1689. Of its tributaries, the River Wissey was mentioned in Domesday Book, though it may not have been the present river of that name, and in 1575 instructions were given by the Commissioners of Sewers for it to be cleansed and widened; perhaps drainage was uppermost in their minds. There were wharves at Oxborough Hithe by the mid-18th century. The Little Ouse was open to Thetford c.1677 and the Cam to Cambridge, navigable in the Middle Ages, was improved by 1702. The River Lark gained its Act in 1700 and had been improved to Bury St Edmunds by c.1720. Another small river, the Nar, joins the Ouse now at King's Lynn, but anciently flowed westwards to Wiggenhall. It was made navigable in 1757-9, under an Act of 1751, by Langley Edwards, who was working on the Ivel Navigation in Bedfordshire at the same time and later would be involved with Kinderley's Cut on the River Nene (**N24**). It had one lock and nine staunches.

Another major navigable river was the Nene. It was improved from Wisbech up to Peterborough under an Act of 1724 and from there to Northampton under an Act of 1756. Although it had fewer tributaries than the Ouse, its importance increased in 1815 when a branch from the Grand Junction Canal joined it at Northampton and provided the only all-water route from East Anglia to the Midlands. Like the Ouse, it was an outlet for substantial quantities of upland water in times of flood, and here, too, there were conflicts between navigation and drainage interests.

In 1852 an Act appointed commissioners to improve the river, with the intention that sea-going vessels might travel up as far as Peterborough and the river be improved from there. J.M. Rendel was appointed Engineer, but there were two divisions of the river, with the upper division subdivided into three, so that there was enormous scope for arguments about the priority of the works. When Rendel died in 1856, (Sir) John Fowler, later the Engineer of the Forth Railway Bridge, succeeded him as Engineer and proceeded to build what were called dams by their opponents but were really staunches, at Waldersea and Guyhirn, and a submerged weir below the bridge in Wisbech. These were designed as temporary measures to protect the river banks, but because the scheme did not proceed they seemed likely to become permanent. Eventually Wisbech Corporation challenged the legality of the dams in the courts and won their case. That night, just as they had done at Kinderley's Cut in 1722, groups of local men went to Waldersea and destroyed the dam there. That at Guyhirn and the throttle at Wisbech were removed in a more legal fashion. Despite the expenditure of nearly £200,000, no work was done above Peterborough, and Wisbech remained the head of navigation for sea-going ships. By 1930 the river was sometimes impassable even for the smallest barges, but the leisure traffic that uses it now does so thanks to the Land Drainage Act of that year, and to the Nene Catchment Board and their successors who upgraded the structures and dredged the river.

The River Waveney was the first in Norfolk to receive an Act of Parliament to improve its navigation, in 1670. Three locks were built, at Wainford, Ellingham and Geldeston in order to extend the navigable waterway from Beccles up to Bungay. The navigation remained much in this state, with many staithes along its banks for local trade, until the 19th century when the merchants of Norwich, fed up like those on the Waveney with the problems of passing through Breydon Water, obtained an Act to create a harbour at Lowestoft (see Chapter 3). The opening of the cut from Lake Lothing to the sea in 1829 shortened and improved the Waveney navigation and trade improved markedly for a time. The locks were similar to those on the River Stour, with wooden sides held apart by overhead portal frames. Like other navigations, the Waveney suffered from competition from railways and then road traffic, and it was closed formally in 1934, but work is now under way to restore it.

The River Stour is well known to many beyond the ranks of waterway enthusiasts from the paintings of John Constable. It was the subject of letters patent from King Charles I in 1628 to make the river navigable, and an Act of 1725 authorised works as far up as Sudbury. The 13 locks were of timber, with portal frames about six feet above water level preventing the side walls from moving inwards; there were also 13 staunches. Competition from the railways saw six of the locks rebuilt but the navigation slowly declined, though in the 1930s the four lowest locks were rebuilt in concrete in return for agreement to the South Essex Water Company's plans to abstract water from the river. Since 1968 there has been progress in restoring parts of the river to leisure traffic.

The River Cam on its course from Clayhithe to Upware receives three artificial waterways, or lodes, on its right bank. Going downstream, these are the Bottisham Lode, the Swaffham and Bulbeck Lode and the **Reach Lode (C26)**; the latter also brings water from the Burwell, Wicken and Monk's Lodes. These waterways start at the fen edge and travel straight, almost parallel to each other, across the fen to the main river. They have traditionally been ascribed to the Romans, and evidence of Roman occupation has been found along the fen edge. However, unsurprisingly, there is no documentary evidence of a Roman origin; nor are the Roman sites immediately adjacent to the heads of the lodes. The Royal Commission in 1972 noted that this origin could not be proved, and more recent publications have suggested a late-Saxon date. Whichever is the case, the waterways today are the result of evolution over the years.

The River Gipping or **Ipswich & Stowmarket Navigation (S11)** was surveyed by William Jessop in 1789, who was then taking over from his old master, John Smeaton, as the leading canal engineer. For a navigation whose principal traffic would be agricultural, Jessop designed simple wooden bridges and locks. Litigation and poor management led the trustees in late 1791 to call in John Rennie, who had looked over the ground from Bury St Edmunds to Ipswich in 1789, as well surveying possible canals from Hadleigh to Mistley, Bury to Mistley and Bury to Hadleigh. Rennie was more concerned with the permanence of his works – a few years later there was a sharp exchange of views between Jessop and Rennie on the subject – and the works from Needham Market down to Ipswich were constructed to higher standards than those above.

6   *Heybridge Basin.*

The Ipswich & Stowmarket was the first navigation that Rennie brought to completion, and it led to his appointment in 1793 as Engineer to the **Chelmer & Blackwater Navigation (E2)**, another fairly minor river with several watermills dependent on it as their source of power. Rennie's solution was the same as on the Gipping for most of its length – a river navigation with bypasses for the mills – but at the lower end he proposed an entirely new cut to bypass Maldon to a new outlet at Heybridge Basin.

The Wisbech Canal was one of only three true canals in the region, and the only one to gain its Act during the canal mania of the early 1790s. It was surveyed by John Watté in 1792, authorised in 1794 and fully open by 9 January 1796. It was unusual in a couple of respects. It was constructed on the line of the ancient Well Stream between Wisbech and Outwell, which had been filled in and in places built upon. Its main water supply came from the tidal River Nene at Wisbech, which caused problems because the silt in the water, once admitted to the canal and stilled, deposited and clogged up the canal. Despite competition from railways, and more particularly from the Wisbech & Upwell Tramway (see below), it was only in 1926 that it was formally abandoned. Ownership was vested in Wisbech Corporation in 1944 and the line filled in again. In Wisbech, Churchill Road (A1101) has been constructed on its bed; motorists on the A1101 through Outwell will notice a road running parallel, with a wide green strip between where the canal once was.

The North Walsham & Dilham Canal is the most northerly of the Broadland navigations, extending the previously navigable River Ant. It was surveyed by John Millington (1779-1868), a polymath who later as a professor in the United States wrote *Elements of Civil Engineering*. This, however, was his only canal and although the Act was passed in 1812, work did not start until 1825. The contractor was Thomas Hughes, who had worked on the Caledonian Canal and other projects in Scotland; the navvies came from Bedfordshire, where, possibly not by coincidence, Millington was county surveyor. The ground conditions were not good for canal construction, being very marshy. Hughes succeeded Millington as Engineer to the canal after it was opened on 29 August 1826, and on the basis of his experience at North Walsham was asked to give evidence on the bill for the **Norwich & Lowestoft Navigation (N10)** the following year.

A late canal, built in 1832 apparently without an Act of Parliament, connected Whitehouse Farm at Mundon with the Blackwater Estuary in Essex. There was a sea lock at its north end.

At the same time a much more ambitious scheme was under construction. Norwich had for many years been dissatisfied with its dependency on Great Yarmouth for navigation. Under the slogan 'Norwich a Port!', a campaign was launched to create an independent route to the sea. The Act was gained in 1827 to make a ship canal, the Norwich & Lowestoft Navigation, from Reedham to Haddiscoe, and cut through the embankment at Mutford and so to a new harbour at Lowestoft. Apart from the **North Level** and **Middle Level Drains (C32, N26)**, whose use for navigation was ancillary to their main function, the Norwich & Lowestoft was the last major canal to be dug in the region.

RAILWAYS

Apart from one line conceived as part of a long-distance route north from London, East Anglia was rather tardy in providing itself with railways. The costs of construction of the two earliest main lines so far outstripped the estimates that each managed to construct less than half of their authorised mileage. One outcome was a group of antagonistic railway companies – the Northern & Eastern, the Eastern Counties, the Eastern Union, the Norfolk and the East Anglian – that only came together by degrees to form the Great Eastern Railway in 1862. This company largely had a monopoly in Norfolk, Suffolk and Essex, disturbed only by the London, Tilbury & Southend Railway in the south, the **Midland & Great Northern Joint Railway (N15)** later in the north, and a few local lines. The Great Eastern had a presence in Cambridgeshire, which was also served by the Great Northern Railway.

One of the earliest proposals for a railway in the region was the London & Essex in 1811. This would have been 43 miles long, from Islington, London, to Wallasea Island and Mucking, and went hand in hand with an unusual scheme to bring sea water by pipeline from Shoebury to baths in London. As with so many later schemes, nimbyism prevailed and it made no progress. In 1824-5, about the time that the Stockton & Darlington Railway was nearing completion, there was a railway mania with no fewer than 72 schemes put forward. East Anglia was not immune, and the plan of Henry Robinson Palmer's London & Ipswich Railway was deposited in 1825. It was similar to the Stockton & Darlington in that it kept gradients to a minimum wherever possible and then used an inclined plane, in its case north of Brentwood, to overcome a significant change of height. When the Eastern Counties Railway was built 18 years later, it went round the south of Brentwood, but still had to climb for more than three miles at gradients up to 1 in 85. Other railways mooted in these two years included the Norfolk, Suffolk & Essex; Bury St Edmunds, Sudbury & Mistleigh; Maldon & Witham; General Railroad (Palmer's patent); Colchester & Halstead; and Ipswich & Suffolk, this one by (Sir) William Cubitt.

Two lines from London were approved by Parliament in 1836, the Northern & Eastern to Cambridge (it had intended to continue to York, but lack of finance prevented it) and the Eastern Counties to Great Yarmouth via Ipswich and Norwich. The Engineer of the former was James Walker, who had been one of the judges at the Rainhill Trials in 1829 and had already completed the Leeds & Selby Railway. However, progress was slow and expensive and Walker resigned in 1839, to be succeeded by Robert Stephenson. The company struggled on to reach Newport in Essex by 1845, but could go no further.

John Braithwaite was another of the three judges at Rainhill, and he was the Engineer of the Eastern Counties Railway. It was noted in an early book on railways that he had determined that the viaduct at the London end of the line 'shall stand for ages, for it is built in a very substantial style'. From there to Brentwood the gradient was no steeper anywhere than 1 in 330, and the line ran alternately on embankment and in cutting. At Brentwood there is an echo of the earlier London & Ipswich Railway, as the gradient steepens to 1 in 103 for two miles before a short length at 1 in 85, quite severe in those days. Brentwood was reached in 1840, with 22 bridges over and 17 under the railway, as well as the London viaduct. They had spent £1¼ million on making 18 miles of line, so further progress was slow. The company was also most unfortunate in its dealing with Lord Petre, a landowner at Ingatestone, who eventually received £124,800 as compensation for disturbance to his peace and quiet. The railway reached Colchester in 1843, when the Board of Trade's inspecting officer commented that it had more bridges and viaducts in its line than almost any other in the country.

The politics of railways in East Anglia then took a curious turn. The Eastern Counties abandoned its line beyond Colchester and obtained powers instead to take over the authorised route of the Northern & Eastern Railway beyond Newport to the small village of Brandon, where it would meet a line being promoted from Norwich. There would also be a line from Ely to Peterborough, to meet the branch that the London & Birmingham Railway was building, and so gain access to the Midlands. The evidence in Parliament for the line was given by Michael Borthwick and he became resident engineer during construction, as he had been on the Northern & Eastern; the contractors were Grissell & Peto.

The first railway in Norfolk was the Yarmouth & Norwich, whose chairman was George Stephenson and Engineer, his son Robert. It went the long way round, following the river via Reedham, in order to keep the line more or less level by avoiding the higher ground. In Norwich a loop in the River Wensum was diverted to flow alongside and to the south of the railway, requiring only low-level, fixed bridges over the old channel. By adopting these measures, the line was built in just over a year. The Norwich & Brandon Railway was promoted by many of the people behind the Yarmouth & Norwich, with whom it would shortly amalgamate under the title of the Norfolk Railway. An interesting reminder of the economics of early railways is the many surviving identical brick and flint houses at the level crossings between Trowse and Thetford. It was cheaper to employ people to open and shut the gates than to build bridges over the line.

The people of Ipswich, having been left high and dry by the Eastern Counties, set about a line of their own. The Eastern Union Railway was engineered by Joseph Locke, with Peter Bruff as the resident engineer, and it opened from an end-on junction with the Eastern Counties at Colchester to Ipswich in 1846. Going north from Ipswich, the first line to be promoted was to Bury St Edmunds, while the line from Colchester was still under construction. At the banquet in Bury to celebrate the first train on 26 November 1846, Bruff stated that:

> although the distance in point of mileage was but small, the difficulties of the line had been great. They had heard of a tunnel they would never get through, and of a bog they would never surmount; yet here they were at Bury within little short of a year. (Loud cheers) In that time they had moved nearly two millions of cubic yards of earth, had built more than 100 bridges and culverts, many of formidable dimensions.

He was not quite accurate, as the work had started at Ipswich 16 months earlier, but perhaps post-prandial speeches are not to be relied upon too much. The bog he referred to was at Stowmarket, where a low embankment had been intended to carry the line over marshy ground just south of the station. After work had been going on for some time, and the embankment had settled slightly as the ground below was compacted, the weight of soil had broken the layer of hard ground below and the embankment had almost disappeared. Because the line from the south was not open to carry fill from the cutting at Badley Hill, the contractor had to find a local source and cart it in. As the material sank it displaced and pushed up the surrounding ground. It took almost three months before success was assured. The relief road under construction in 2009 is suffering from the same trouble. Just north of Stowmarket there was a similar problem, but a cutting a short distance further north could supply the extra fill; the extra width on the east side of the line is still visible today. The nature of the problem can be appreciated from the fact that at the nearby site of the bridge over the River Gipping, 45ft timber piles sank under their own weight, and it was found that no solid ground could be found for a depth of 80ft. The decision was made to divert the river instead, where it can still be seen west of the line.

It is interesting to note that a clergyman at the banquet

> acknowledged that when this railroad was first projected, he for one anticipated it would be a fruitful source of crime; but he had been agreeably disappointed; and he must say he did not think a similar number of men had ever been gathered together who had done less mischief than the operatives of this line. (Loud cheers) He thought that this was highly creditable both to them and to their superiors. (Cheers)

The contractor for the Ipswich & Bury Railway, and also for both stretches of the Eastern Union main line, was Thomas Brassey, but the work here was supervised by his partner Alexander Ogilvie, originally from Scotland but who settled later at Sizewell Hall in Suffolk.

The subcontractor who had been responsible for the work at Stowmarket also took the length of the Eastern Union extension to Norwich from the junction at Haughley to Burston, a couple of miles north of Diss. This stretch included the embankment over Thrandeston Bog, south of Diss, where even in 2008 it was necessary to undertake dry soil mixing to improve the stability of the embankment. The 60ft-deep cutting at Markshall, now crossed by the A47 Norwich bypass, was entrusted to the subcontractor who had dug the Brantham cutting on the original Eastern Union line. The contemporary picture of Bull Bridge under construction shows how the soil was wheeled out along a shelf on the side of the cutting, rather than being barrowed up the sides as in the famous engraving of Tring Cutting on the London & Birmingham Railway.

7 *Brantham Cutting, Eastern Union Railway, Illustrated London News.*

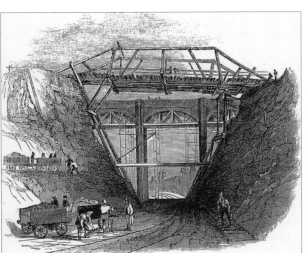

The first railway to Lowestoft was part of a larger scheme promoted by (Sir) Samuel Morton Peto to revive the harbour there and create a new seaside resort. It required two swing bridges, over the navigable Rivers Yare and Waveney which, although a retractable bridge had been built about ten years earlier for the London & Birmingham Railway over a branch of the Grand Junction Canal, were among the first large movable bridges on a British railway. The line was opened in 1847.

The failure of the Northern & Eastern Railway to raise funds for its line to York has been noted. There was, however, a route between London and

8 *Wisbech & Upwell Tramway.*

the North-East of England from 1840, over the lines of four companies via Rugby and Derby. To create a more direct route, the Great Northern Railway was authorised in 1846, after an unsuccessful attempt the previous year, to go via Peterborough and Doncaster. In East Anglia its only problem was the line over Holme Fen, south of Peterborough, which was dealt with by the same means that had been employed 20 years earlier at Chat Moss on the Liverpool & Manchester Railway.

The railway map of East Anglia at its fullest still showed some surprising gaps. Although there were several proposals for one, there was never a direct line between Norwich and East Dereham, the latter being served by a branch from Wymondham. On the Norfolk coast, again despite plans for others, the only port served by rail was Wells-next-the Sea.

An oddity was the Wisbech & Upwell tramway, built by the Great Eastern Railway in 1882-4. For much of its length it ran beside the Wisbech Canal (see above) and because it was laid in the public road, its locomotives were required to have cowcatchers at both ends and their wheels protected by side boards. Its primary purpose was the carriage of fruit and vegetables to the main line for onward transport. Its success in this respect was a significant factor in the legislation which allowed the creation of light railways in the UK.

In the 20th century the lines to Harwich and Walton/Clacton were among the earliest to be electrified on the overhead 25kV system. Subsequently the wires were extended to Norwich, over the east coast main line and to King's Lynn. Some heritage of the original railways, particularly overbridges, was lost as a result, but much still remains in the region.

Compared with some other regions of Britain, East Anglia has few of the really outstanding bridges of historical merit. Nevertheless, there is a good variety of form, material and age to interest the observer. There is a noticeable scarcity of stone bridges in the area east of the limestone belt in north-west Cambridgeshire, but this is compensated by the survival of several brick bridges that are among the earliest in the country. The River Waveney can boast the nation's oldest surviving concrete bridge.

Ascribing dates to bridges built before the middle of the 18th century is difficult to do with any degree of certainty, because of the lack of contemporary records. Even where accounts do exist, the present structure may be a subsequent rebuilding that has passed unrecorded. It is necessary therefore to look at the structure itself. Unfortunately there were no clear transitions from one style to another as in, say, church architecture. Some clues may be found in the arch shape. The earliest were either semi-circular, in the Romanesque tradition, or curved-pointed Gothic arches. As time went on, the rise of the arch became less, and the arches became 'flat-pointed'. From the 14th century segmental arches enabled the construction of flatter and therefore less steep approaches, important when the motive power was provided by horses.

The problems of identification are made more difficult in the case of **Huntingdon Bridge (C21)** over the river Great Ouse. In its six arches there are four different styles of construction. The date of one is known — it was broken down in 1645 and replaced by a drawbridge, which in turn was rebuilt with a segmental stone arch. The other arches are flat-pointed, but the arch nearest the town is much lower than the others and the second and third arches have architectural features on the west face that are absent from the two southern arches. Various authorities have given different 14th-century dates for this structure.

One of the most unusual bridges in the country crosses the river Great Ouse a few miles downstream, in St Ives (**C27**). The construction of a bridge in medieval times was a substantial undertaking, often requiring the resources of a religious house, municipal guild or major landowner. Once built, the fabric would require maintenance, which on occasion was provided by a resident priest, who would collect alms to pay for the necessary work and officiate at a chapel on or close by the bridge where prayers could be said for the souls of the donors. St Ives is one of only three or four to retain its chapel, the others being at Wakefield, Rotherham and possibly Bradford-on-Avon. The bridge itself was mentioned in 1259 and was of timber when it was recorded again in 1384. The chapel, which appears to be contemporary with the rebuilding of the bridge in stone, was dedicated to St Leger by the Abbot of Ramsey in 1426.

Bishop Bridge (N16) in Norwich once supported another type of structure, one of the gates that formed part of the city's defences. The bridge was repaired in 1249, and in 1275 a patent was granted to William de Kerkeby to build a gate with bridge adjoining. The present bridge, when it was built by Richard Spynk in 1337-41, was the first in the city to be built of stone. The gatehouse was removed in 1791, but evidence of its supports can still be seen above the cutwaters. The only remaining example is at Monmouth.

Bishop Bridge has the remains of three of its original five ribs under its arches, a style of construction whose purpose in bridges is not entirely clear. The ribs of those in East Anglia are chamfered, like those in the arches of church arcades, which required a high standard of workmanship. The extra cost of this workmanship might have been offset by a need for the centering during construction to be only the width of one or two ribs,

13

thus saving the cost of materials, but this would imply that the stones of the main arch would be sufficiently long to span between the ribs, which is not always the case. Ribbed bridges are more common in Britain than on the Continent, and more common in the north and west of England than the south, but there are nevertheless several other examples in East Anglia. Of these, Harold's Bridge at Waltham Abbey (TL 381007) may well be monastic in origin. At **Huntingdon Bridge (C21)** the arch nearest the town has been widened, apparently by building a rib at the outer edge of the new structure, then spanning from it back to the original work. The other bridges are 14th- or more probably 15th-century but have little in common with each other, either in the shape of the ribs or in their spacing. Spaldwick Bridge (TL 127730) has three ribs with deep chamfers and the space between them is more than four times the width of the ribs. **Wiveton Bridge (N28)**, though, has five ribs almost as wide as their spacing. In neither of these two do the main arch stones span across from one rib to the next. **St Ives Bridge (C27)** has five ribs, Newton Flotman (TM 212979) four, Potter Heigham (TG 420185) four and Toppesfield at Hadleigh (TM 026422) six. The small bridge in Littleport Street at King's Lynn (TF 626203) is one of only two in the country to have two tiers of chamfered ribs; it may have been built in the 1440s at the same time as the adjacent East Gate. A curiosity is Abbot's Bridge over the River Lark at Bury

9 *Huntingdon Bridge, seen from downstream.*

10 *St Ives Bridge, before restoration of the bridge chapel.*

11 *Abbot's Bridge, Bury St Edmunds.*

12 *Pleshey Castle Bridge.*

St Edmunds. The Abbey precinct wall is carried on pointed arches, each with two ribs; alongside and springing from the same piers are segmental arches carrying a footpath within the precinct, while outside there are buttresses to the walls with passageways through them, presumably to allow a removable timber plank bridge.

Gothic arches became flatter as time progressed, but the perils of relying too much on arch shape for dating bridges is shown in the case of the brick bridge over the moat of Pleshey Castle in Essex (TL 665144). This is attributed to the middle of the 15th century but has a sharp-pointed arch, though this may be due to the unusual height of the bridge for its time. Other bridges over the (now dry) moats of medieval castles remain at Castle Rising and Castle Hedingham. It has been suggested that the latter was built for the reception of Henry VII on a visit in 1498. The shape of its four arches is in transition from the pointed to the Tudor and though each arch spans only 10ft, it is a substantial piece of work with triple arch rings.

There are very few packhorse bridges remaining in East Anglia. Indeed, that over the River Kennett at Moulton in Suffolk (**S9**) is the only one that can be claimed with confidence. The one called the Packhorse Bridge in the grounds of the Abbey at Walsingham is almost certainly not.

In the 16th century pointed arches gave way to four-centred, perpendicular or Tudor shapes. An interesting example in the region is **Mayton Bridge (N3)** over an old branch of the river Bure near Buxton. Lack of suitable stone meant that it was built of brick and its four-centred arches are an unusual feature in brick bridges. There is a small shelter in each of the upstream wingwalls, a unique feature whose true purpose is not clear. Until the 1930s at least, the bridge over the main river had a timber superstructure.

Wansford Old Bridge (C34) shows evidence of three distinct building phases, on each subsequent occasion creating higher and larger arches to cope with navigation and floods in the River Nene. The first phase has a stone inscribed with the date '1577'.

13 *Wansford Old Bridge, date stone.*

14   *Cooke's Bridge, Godmanchester.*

15 *Adam Bridge, Audley End.*

16 *Tea House Bridge, Audley End.*

The largest of its arches is a rebuild dated '1795' when two arches destroyed by flood were turned into one. Even so, in times of greatest flood, powered boats going upstream cannot make headway against the current.

To deal with excess water in the River Ouse, the southern approach to Huntingdon Bridge is over an embankment with two eight-arch brick bridges in it. The Causeway (TL 243712) was constructed in 1637 by Robert Cooke, but reconstruction took place in 1767 and again in 1784. An inscribed stone in the parapet is a modern copy of an original. Even more extensive is the New Bridge, the southern approach to St Ives Bridge, with 51 arches dating from 1822.

Few notable bridges were built in England during the last three quarters of the 17th century, a time of civil and political unrest. Some, like Huntingdon and St Ives, had an arch destroyed for defence during the Civil War and were repaired subsequently. The finest bridge of the period in East Anglia was a private bridge, built by a Cambridge college over the River Cam. **Clare College Bridge (C3)** was built in 1638-40 and is the oldest remaining along the Backs. Though not large – the central of its three segmental arches spans only 21ft 6in – it is highly architectural, and is said to have the first classical balustrade to be built in England. The River Welland is unusual in having five 17th-century bridges over it within a relatively short distance. Uffington Bridge looks medieval but is late 17th-century, possibly built to allow the diversion of a drovers' route when Uffington House was built in the 1680s. By the time the river reaches Maxey it runs in several channels, each with its own small bridge over it. Called **Lolham Bridges (C22)**, three are dated '1641', '1652' and '1699'; others are 18th-century. **Deeping Gate Bridge (C12)**, where the river has reverted to a single waterway, is dated '1651'. It is a substantial structure, but the largest of its three arches spans only 19ft 6in.

The second oldest bridge over the Cambridge Backs, **St John's College Old Bridge (C7)**, was built in 1712 and is even more ornate than Clare College Bridge. It was designed and built by Robert Grumbold, a member of a long-established family of stonemasons from Weldon and Raunds in Northamptonshire, and whose forebear Thomas Grumbold had been master mason at Clare. A much more restrained design is that of **Ferry Bridge (C11)**, Castor, of 1716, originally a private bridge built for the 1st Earl Fitzwilliam of nearby Milton Hall. It was probably the most expensive toll bridge in the country, the charge amounting to about three days wages for a labourer at the time.

Elliptical arches were introduced to Britain in the 1760s after a fierce architectural debate about the aesthetics of the proposed Blackfriars Bridge in London. Cambridge was well up with the fashion in this, the replacement of **Trinity College Bridge (C8)** in 1764-5 to the design of James Essex exhibiting this feature. An altogether more subtle design than Clare or St John's Old, it uses stone of slightly different colour from Northamptonshire and Dorset to differentiate the structural elements of the bridge. Essex was probably aware of Adam Bridge, built in 1763-4 to carry the public road over the River Cam at Audley End (TL 521380). This bridge derives its name from its architect, the well-known Robert Adam, who was remodelling the nearby house, and he detailed the spandrel walls in a different stone from the arch rings; the balustrade is similar in colour to the latter, but is a replacement of c.1781. The park at Audley End was laid out by Capability Brown in 1763-6 and over the years Adam contributed designs for some of the eyecatchers there. His Tea House Bridge was built in 1782-3 and carries an elegant summerhouse with Ionic columns on a segmental arch, all in fine ashlar.

Legal responsibility for the upkeep of bridges rested with those who had tradition-ally maintained them, or with corporate bodies such as towns with charters; failing them, the justices of the peace in the Court of Quarter Sessions in each county carried the burden. Under the Statute of Bridges passed in 1531, when the public considered that a bridge was out of repair they would 'present' it to the court, who would consider the presentment at the next Quarter Sessions. The court would decide whether the

17 Lolham Bridges, Maxey, date stone.

bridge was indeed out of repair and, if so, who was responsible for its maintenance. An order to repair would be made against those responsible and if at subsequent Quarter Sessions no action had been taken, a fine would be levied and used to put the bridge in order. Only if a bridge was of use to the general public and no other body could be shown to be liable would the county repair it. This charge was not very welcome to the justices, who would normally wish to escape responsibil-ity. Lolham Bridges at Maxey (mentioned above) are unusual in that two of the bridges have 17th-century inscriptions recording that they were built by the county.

18 Cattawade Bridge.

The first mention of county surveyors is made in the 1531 Statute of Bridges. The county justices were required to ensure that the bridge stock was kept in good repair, and to assist them they were permitted to appoint two surveyors, who were to 'see every such decayed bridge repaired and amended from time to time, as often as the need shall require'. It would seem that no surveyor was in fact appointed until c.1684, when Northumberland was the first to do so; Essex was next, in 1704. Norfolk appointed William Ivory, a Norwich architect, in 1773, and Suffolk in 1785 employed Thomas Fulcher, a carpenter and builder of Ipswich. Subsequently each division in Suffolk employed a surveyor, though some individuals held several appointments. The Suffolk part of Cattawade Bridge dates from c.1791 (TM 101330). Thomas Lovell was county surveyor of Huntingdonshire, which was a county in its own right, by 1843, when Earith Bridge was being rebuilt. Cambridgeshire was the last county in the region to make an appointment, the architect W.M. Milner Fawcett, in 1862. Over time, the duties of the county surveyors extended beyond merely surveying and reporting on the condition of the bridges, to planning and organising repairs, and designing and supervising the construction of new ones.

Not all 19th-century bridges were built by the county, however. The North Level of the Fens

19 *Cloughs Cross Bridge and Sluice, under repair.*

20 *Benwick Old Bridge.*

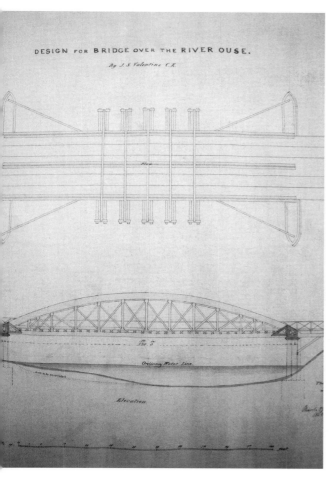

DESIGN FOR BRIDGE OVER THE RIVER OUSE.

By J. S. Valentine C.E.

obtained a much improved drainage in 1829-34 (see Chapter 5), which included many new internal drains. Several of the bridges over these drains have elegant brick arches with a keystone recording the date of construction. The bridge at Cloughs Cross (TF 368093) spans the New South Eau and the New Wryde where they join to form the North Level Main Drain, and contains the remains of sluices and wharves.

Timber was used for many of the early bridges in East Anglia. Many of these were trestle structures of small span on timber piles, sometimes with knee braces to reduce the unsupported length of the main timber beams. Even as late as 1858 in Essex, 18 of the 70 county bridges were still wholly of wood or had wooden superstructures on brick abutments. Many had been built to the designs of John Johnson, who was County Surveyor from 1782 to 1812 and rebuilt nearly 50 bridges, of which 14 were of timber. Some of these may have been built because of difficulty in finding adequate ground to carry the abutments of an arch, but cost seems also to have been a major issue, as when Johnson provided alternative designs in brick and timber for Widford in 1803 and the latter was chosen. Because timber is generally less durable than masonry or iron, these structures have almost entirely disappeared, though an example can still be found at Benwick (TL 341906).

21 *Hilgay Bridge, Lynn & Ely Railway (Cambridgeshire Record Office R59/31/40/143)*

The same consideration was also to the fore when the early railways were being built. The Eastern Union Railway crossed the River Stour at Cattawade by two long viaducts of timber, mostly simple trestle spans but with a truss over the navigable channel; they were replaced only in 1904. Another long-lived wooden railway bridge was that over the River Wissey on the Lynn & Ely Railway. The same line boasted a fine laminated timber bowstring arch of 121ft 6in span over the River Ouse at Hilgay, designed by John Valentine, but that lasted only until 1852. The Eastern Counties branch to Peterborough crossed the River Nene near that city on a wooden viaduct that was finally rebuilt in the 1970s. The Maldon, Witham & Braintree Railway, like the Eastern Union with Joseph Locke as Engineer, had six timber viaducts on its line. One of these, at Wickham Bishops (**E14**), now split into two by a later infill embankment, is the only railway example known to remain in England, though there a few fine examples in Wales.

Two wooden footbridges of more ornamental appearance still exist in the region. The better known is the **Queens' College or Mathematical Bridge (C6)** at Cambridge, which despite appearing at first sight to be an arch is in fact a truss with a pronounced rise towards the middle. Strangely, in view of the reputed rivalry between the ancient university towns, there is a replica over the River Thames at Iffley, Oxford. The other East Anglian structure is the **Chinese Bridge (C17)** over the River Ouse at Godmanchester, and it is indeed an arch. At 60ft span, it is half as long again as the Mathematical Bridge.

The first cast-iron bridge was erected at Coalbrookdale in Shropshire in 1779, with a span of just over 100ft. Each rib of the main arch comprised two long quarter-circles, resting on the abutments and meeting at the crown. They supported subsidiary arch rings and spandrel infill; its detailing owed much to carpentry practice. Although technically successful, its constructors suffered significant financial loss, which appears to have dampened enthusiasm for the new material. Nevertheless, a bridge of 236ft span was completed over the River Wear at Sunderland in 1796. This was based on a patent that envisaged the arch rings formed of cast-iron pieces more akin to the voussoirs of a masonry bridge.

Cast-iron bridges in the East of England were, with few exceptions, not particularly adventurous. One exception was the bridge now in the grounds of Culford School, Suffolk (**S3**). It was built in 1803-4 based on a patent awarded to Samuel Wyatt, a prominent architect and civil engineer, in 1800. It is the only known example in Britain of a cast-iron arch with hollow tubular ribs. The difficulties of manufacturing the components meant that it came from a foundry in Gateshead, County Durham. 1804 also saw the construction of a cast-iron bridge over the River Wensum in Norwich, known variously as St Miles' Bridge, St Michael's Bridge or **Coslany Bridge (N18)**. Built under a design-and-build contract with James Frost junior, a local carpenter, the design benefited from input from the leading civil engineer William Jessop. It has a span of 36ft and was built in a little under nine months from award of contract.

The next cast-iron bridge known to have been erected in the region is in the grounds of Rochetts, near Brentwood, designed by John Rennie senior. The owner of the house at the time, 1809, was Earl St Vincent, who had been First Lord of the Admiralty and in that capacity had worked with Rennie in upgrading the naval dockyards on the River Thames. Of moderate span only, it is interesting in that it marks a break away from Rennie's previous practice (Town Bridge, Boston, Lincolnshire, rebuilt in 1912, and several abortive schemes for spans up to 350ft) of using cast-iron voussoirs in the Sunderland tradition. It is visible only with the permission of the owner. The same year saw a second cast-iron bridge in Norwich, at Carrow. It was designed by a local architect, Arthur Browne, and the ironwork was cast by J.G. Aggs.

The years 1811-12 saw a significant advance in the design of cast-iron bridges, when Bonar Bridge in the north of Scotland was built to a design by Thomas Telford. This had a span of 150ft and made full use of the properties of cast iron to develop a design that did not hark back to timber or masonry experience. The main arch ribs were cast in five segments only and the spandrels used lozenge-framed struts and bracing to support the road deck. In 1812, (Sir) William Cubitt was employed by the established Ipswich company Ransome & Son to develop their civil engineering work, and over the next two years they built three small cast-iron bridges in Suffolk and Essex, at Brent Eleigh, Clare (**S2**) and Witham, contracts that the company acknowledged 'would probably not have been undertaken without him'. Their design is by no means as sophisticated as Telford's, but Cubitt may have been constrained by the capacity of Ransome's foundry; Telford had the advantage of William Hazledine's purpose-built works at Plas Kynaston. All three East Anglian bridges still exist, although Brent Eleigh has been bypassed and Saul's Bridge at Witham has been strengthened. Stoke Bridge at Ipswich, by Cubitt and Ransome's, was built in 1818-19. It was significantly larger than the three earlier bridges, with a 60ft span, but technically still in the line of descent from the Coslany Bridge at Norwich. It was demolished in 1925. A variation on this theme is the bridge of 1818 over the River Wensum at Hellesdon, outside Norwich, which has three large ribs supporting the cast-iron trough that carries the roadway. At 38ft 6in, its span is only 2ft 6in longer than that at Coslany, but it is interesting as it shows the development of the thinking

22 *Hellesdon Bridge.*

of its design-and-build contractor, James Frost, who had also been responsible for the earlier bridge. Still in this tradition is **Magdalene, or Great, Bridge (C5)** at Cambridge, on the site of the original bridge that gave the town its name. It was said to have been designed by the same Arthur Browne who had earlier designed Carrow Bridge at Norwich, but it is known that Benjamin Bevan of Leighton Buzzard also had some input. He had already had experience in cast iron, having rebuilt the Ouse Aqueduct of the Grand Junction Canal at Wolverton in 1811 in that material.

The question of who actually designed these cast-iron bridges has not been satisfactorily resolved. Two examples in the region, both now demolished, were illustrated in a contemporary book on 'modern' bridges. High Bridge over the River Ouse at Ely, on the site of the ancient crossing to Stuntney and Soham, was rebuilt in 1833. It was ascribed to Joseph Glynn, who was the engineer of the Butterley Company in Derbyshire. That company was one of the earliest to have supplied and erected cast-iron bridges, its predecessor having erected the first cast-iron aqueduct, at Derby in 1796. Glynn had joined Butterley about 1821 and had developed their steam engine business as well as the structural use of cast iron. The 1837 Garret Hostel Bridge at Cambridge is credited to William Chadwell Mylne, but Glynn's obituary in the Minutes of Proceedings of the Institution of Civil Engineers states that, as well as Ely, he was responsible for its design, and a comparison of the drawings in the book shows indeed that at least the detail design for both must have been from a common source. It may well be that the nominal designers, such as Browne and Mylne, decided the architectural form only and the founders such as Butterley did the structural design.

Town Bridge (N19) at Thetford has the date '1829' cast on it. It was designed by Francis Stone, the county surveyor, and erected by the London firm of Bough & Smith, who built cast-iron bridges elsewhere in the country. In the same year Stone and Bough & Smith were also responsible for the similar Fye Bridge at Norwich. Town Bridge still exists, but Fye, after being widened in 1921, was rebuilt in 1933.

The later cast-iron bridges in East Anglia were generally smaller and less ambitious, and were the products of local foundries. In Cambridgeshire the bridge at Somersham

23 *Garret Hostel Bridge, Cambridge (1837).*

was cast by Headly at the Eagle Foundry in 1844. Four small bridges over Hobson's Conduit in Brookside, Cambridge, were cast in 1850-1 by Hurrell, who were also responsible for the bridge at Melbourn in 1866. Essex, by contrast, had several foundries willing to turn their hand to castings for bridges. The earliest bridge in the old county, for the Commercial Road Trust over the River Lea, was designed by James Walker, Thomas Telford's successor as President of the Institution of Civil Engineers. The next was Saul's Bridge at Witham, mentioned above. In 1819 Thomas Hopper, who had succeeded John Johnson as county

24 *North Bridge, Colchester.*

surveyor but was here acting in a private capacity as consultant to the Essex Turnpike Trust, designed a cast-iron bridge but instead a suspension bridge to his own design was built by Ralph Dodd, an enthusiastic but unsuccessful engineer/entrepreneur. It immediately proved inadequate and was repaired by John Richmond, a Chelmsford founder. The timber bridge at Fullbridge, Maldon, was widened in cast iron in 1824-5 by Richard Coleman of Colchester; it was replaced in 1876. He was rather more successful in 1843 with the North Bridge at Colchester; the plaque on it now records its widening in 1903. Under Henry Stock, county surveyor from 1856, several cast-iron bridges were built, including Littlebury (TL 518397) (1858), Nunnery Bridge at Castle Hedingham (TL 777355) and Barfield Bridge at Bulmer (TL 847421) (both 1870, by Symington & Atterton of Halstead), Howe Street Bridge at Great Waltham (TL 699147) (1871 by Coleman & Morton of Chelmsford) and a small bridge at Billericay (TQ 657963) (1873, also by Coleman & Morton).

The largest of these later cast-iron bridges was **St Olaves Bridge (N11)** at Haddiscoe, designed by George Edwards. This is a bowstring girder of 8oft span, one of only two with a cast-iron arch in Britain. A bridge of this size was beyond the capabilities of the local foundries and was supplied from the Regent's Canal Ironworks in London.

In Suffolk Richard Garrett of Leiston was one of the two contractors for Wickham Bridge in 1838, and on his own at East Bridge in 1848 (both cast-iron girder structures), Blythburgh, 1851 (an arch with a 'keystone' dated 1850), and Barking Bridge at Coddenham, 1853 (girders again). They have been rebuilt but two cast-iron girders with deck plates from the bridge of 1843 have been preserved beside the replacement at the north end of Hadleigh. Garrett's bridge of 1851 at Great Thurlow (TL 932482) is still in place, though now strengthened. The 1866 nameplate of 'R Boby of Bury St Edmunds' is still on Flempton Bridge (TL 817703), their only known venture into bridge building. Rural Norfolk has some of the latest cast-iron bridges erected anywhere in Britain; that at Worthing (TF 998201) was built in 1903.

The Great Northern Railway between London and Peterborough had two large cast-iron underbridges, over the River Ouse at Huntingdon and the River Nene at Peterborough (**C24**). The former was replaced in the 1930s but the latter survives, strengthened, one of only three that still carry main line traffic.

Masonry (including brick) viaducts are relatively rare in East Anglia. The Eastern Counties Railway was authorised from London via Ipswich and Norwich to Great Yarmouth by an Act of 1836 but proved to be an expensive line to build. One reason, noted by the inspecting officer shortly before it opened to Colchester in 1843, was that it 'intersects the courses of all the little rivers and crosses the valleys through which they flow. Hence it has a greater number of considerable cuttings and embankments, and has more arches and viaducts ... than perhaps any other line of railway of equal extent.' The line beyond Colchester was built by the Eastern Union Railway, and the need for economy meant the line had to fit more closely to the lie of the land. On other lines in the region, the relatively gentle contours meant there was little need for large railway viaducts. Indeed, only Lakenham Viaduct on the Eastern Union Railway outside Norwich (TG 228052) and **Chappel Viaduct (E1)** on the Colchester, Stour Valley, Sudbury & Halstead Railway bear comparison with the major viaducts elsewhere in the country. Both were built in 1847-9. Lakenham was designed by Joseph Locke, one of the three leading railway engineers of the 1840s, to have six segmental arches of 42 to 45ft span over the River Yare and the Eastern Counties line from London to Norwich via Cambridge. The main line is now via Ipswich and trains travel over this viaduct before turning downhill to join the older line and travel into Trowse Station. Its construction was supervised by the resident engineer, Peter Bruff, who was also the Engineer for the Stour Valley line. Other substantial bridges span the Ipswich line at Brentwood and Brantham, in both cases over deep cuttings necessary to keep the railway gradients within the bounds of the locomotive technology of the time. The one at Brentwood (TQ 600930) has seven

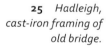

arches, the central one wider than the others, but when the railway was widened from two lines to four, the cutting was scaled back and an extra line run through each of the third and fifth arches.

An interesting wrought iron railway bridge, possibly unique, is the **Vauxhall Bridge (N9)** over the River Bure at Great Yarmouth. Originally opened in 1852 as a box girder, it was converted to a bowstring girder in 1886 by the addition of three parallel arches above. The main bridge has been closed to traffic and only the footpath alongside, part of the 1886 modifications, continues in use. Another interesting conversion, now demolished, spanned the River Ouse at Earith. Originally it was a suspension bridge of 120ft span designed by Captain Sir Samuel Brown in 1842 and built by Fox, Henderson & Co. in 1843-4. It was in danger of collapse by 1863, presumably because the anchorages were pulling out of the soft ground. W.H. Barlow, a

25 *Hadleigh, cast-iron framing of old bridge.*

26 *Great Thurlow Bridge.*

well-known railway engineer who was at the same time jointly responsible for completion of the Clifton Suspension Bridge at Bristol, designed arched booms to span between the tops of the suspension bridge piers, thus converting the structure to a lenticular truss, a quarter-size version of Brunel's Royal Albert Bridge at Saltash. Brown was also responsible for the suspension bridge further down the New Bedford River at Welney. That lasted longer, but was replaced in the 1920s.

The first concrete bridge in Britain was erected over the Metropolitan Railway near Gloucester Road in London in 1868, but it had a short life, not because of any fault in the structure but because it stood in the way of railway developments in that area. The oldest remaining concrete bridge in the country therefore is the one built two years later over the River Waveney at Homersfield (**S5**). It was a mass concrete structure, and East Anglia also has the mass concrete bridge with the largest span – 109ft – at Wansford (**C33**), west of Peterborough. Mass concrete, though, was normally less economic than reinforced concrete after the introduction of the latter into the UK from 1897. The pioneer in this new material was L.G. Mouchel, a French engineer based at first in Swansea and whose early work was therefore more biased towards the west side of the country. One significant boost to its introduction into East Anglia was given by the floods in the River Bure in 1912, by which more than 50 bridges were initially thought to have been destroyed, though some in fact were capable of repair. In order to replace such a large number of bridges in quick time, a standard design was evolved; the bridge at Thurning was described in detail in an article in *Surveyor and Municipal and County Engineer* on 2 June 1916.

27 *Earith Bridge, as strengthened (now replaced).*

Prestressed concrete was first used in a British bridge during the Second World War, but had to wait until the 1950s for engineers to become sufficiently confident to design in significant numbers. Its principal advantage over reinforced concrete in the austerity after the war was that it used less material; the corresponding disadvantage was that the steel and the concrete needed to be of higher quality than in conventional reinforced structures if the benefits of prestressing were to be obtained. The lightness that could be achieved in a medium-span bridge is seen clearly in **Garret Hostel Bridge (C4)**, Cambridge. The largest prestressed concrete bridge in the region is the Orwell Bridge at Ipswich. Its 190m span would not have been possible in reinforced concrete without intruding on the air draught of the ships passing below.

A special class of bridges is that of movable bridges. Where traffic requires to pass under a bridge and it is not possible economically to provide sufficient headroom, the bridge must be made to move out of the way when passage is required. The potential difference in scale between a movable and a fixed bridge can be seen at Haddiscoe (TM 453991), where the swing bridge of the Norwich & Lowestoft Navigation has been replaced by a high-level viaduct.

One of the earliest in the region would have been the Haven Bridge over the River Yare at Great Yarmouth (TG 521074), built first in 1427. The present bridge is the fifth on the site and is a Scherzer rolling lift bridge, opened in 1930. The first bridge at Lowestoft, by contrast, was not built until 1830, when the port was created. That structure was a swing bridge, as was its replacement of 1896, which lasted until it jammed open in 1970, completely separating the two parts of the town until a passenger ferry could be introduced. Its replacement, the present structure, is a bascule bridge, as is the bridge at Mutford that vehicles had to use while Lowestoft was being rebuilt.

There had long been a desire for an all-weather route from Norfolk to the Midlands, on the route now taken by the A17. The River Welland had been bridged at Fosdyke in 1811 and the River Ouse at King's Lynn (TF 612185) in 1823 as part of the Eau Brink project. When the **Nene Outfall (L1)** scheme was proposed in 1825, which involved extensive reclamation of the eastern side of the estuary, local landowners proposed a bridge across it to fill in the last gap in the route. Known as Cross Keys Bridge, from the inn of that name at the eastern edge of the estuary, then over a mile away, it was designed by (Sir) John Rennie. There were approach viaducts of timber trestle structures but the section over the navigable channel was a cast-iron twin-leaf bascule, giving 26ft clearance when the leaves were raised. As so often the case with new works affecting the navigation, the merchants of Wisbech opposed it, and had a clause inserted in the Act requiring the piles supporting the bascules to be driven before the new river channel was excavated. It proved difficult to drive the piles to a sufficient depth, and when the water was turned into the new channel, it scoured out the bed so much as to threaten to undermine the bridge. Large quantities of stones were tipped into the river to shore up the bridge, but they caused turbulence that made navigation difficult. By 1850 it was necessary to replace it and a swing bridge was designed, nominally by

Robert Stephenson, but in fact by his cousin and partner, George Robert Stephenson. It was a wrought-iron box girder 192ft 9in long, on a site 100yds to the south of the old bridge, and, like its predecessor, was operated manually. In 1863 the Lynn & Sutton Bridge Railway (later part of the Midland & Great Northern Joint Railway) acquired powers to purchase the bridge and use it for both road and rail traffic. The railway was opened in 1866. This bridge was replaced, a further 100m to the south, in 1894-7 by the present structure, built by Handyside & Co. of Derby; the hydraulic machinery by Sir William Armstrong & Co. of Newcastle was powered by accumulators in a tower that still stands beside the road south-west of the bridge, but the machinery is now electrical. The railway was closed in 1959 and in 1963 the southern half of the bridge was converted to road use. The positions of the two earlier bridges can be made out from the closed-off road approaches to them.

At Wisbech the 1759 arch bridge rose very steeply to its crown in order to allow navigation below, and there were several serious accidents when horses were unable to control their wagons coming down. As part of the Nene Valley Improvement, J.M. Rendel designed an iron box-girder swing bridge with a clear span of 121ft. It was built by the Regent's Canal Ironworks of London, with hydraulic machinery by Sir William Armstrong & Co. Because the navigation improvements to Peterborough did not take place, it was swung once only as a trial, six days before it was opened on 9 November 1857. It was replaced by a reinforced concrete portal bridge in 1929-31, but one of its four corner plinths remains on the western bank beside the new structure.

Crossings of navigable waterways present particular problems for railways, because the need to keep gradients within acceptable limits means that approach embankments to fixed bridges can be very long and expensive to build and operate. The first railway in Norfolk, the Yarmouth & Norwich, avoided the problem by cutting off a loop in the navigable River Yare, but its sister company, the Norwich & Brandon, required

28 *Elevation of Cross Keys (1830) Bridge and longitudinal section of the River Nene at the bridge. (Cambridgeshire Record Office, R7661/109)*

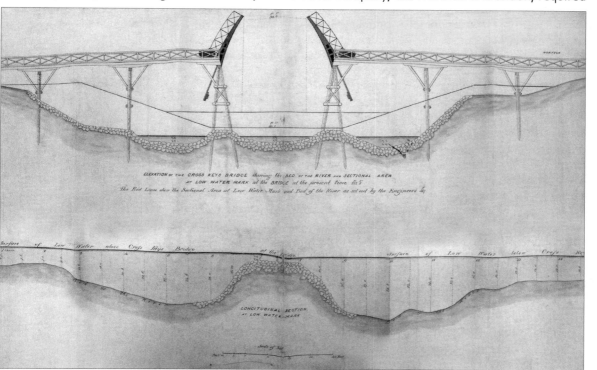

a swing bridge at Trowse in order to reach the joint station at Norwich Thorpe. This bridge was designed by G.P. Bidder as a cast-iron cable-stayed structure that swung about a central pivot, and it was opened in December 1845. In order to join the Yarmouth line, the Lowestoft Railway & Harbour Co. required swing bridges over the River Waveney at Somerleyton and the River Yare at Reedham **(N20)**. As the Engineer to the company was the same G.P. Bidder, the bridges were very similar to that at Trowse, the spans being only slightly different. The main contractors for the railways were Grissell & Peto, in which Thomas Grissell was one of the partners; the bridges were built by the Regent's Canal Ironworks, owned by Thomas's younger brothers, Henry and Martin.

29 *Wisbech Bridge (1857).*

The Trowse Bridge was replaced in 1906, and again in 1984-7 as part of the electrification of the East Anglian main line. It is believed to be the only swing bridge in the world with overhead electrification. The 1906 bridge was followed the next year by the rebuilding of **Oulton Broad Railway Bridge (S8)** to the same design; that bridge still exists. The bridges at Reedham and Somerleyton were rebuilt in 1905 to a different design.

The last railway swing bridge to be built in the region was the Breydon Water Bridge of the Midland & Great Northern Joint. It was constructed in 1900-3 and demolished in 1962 after the line had closed. The site is now occupied by the Dutch-style bascule bridge that takes the A12 out of Great Yarmouth. Its elegant span of 31m was 50 per cent greater than any previous structure of the type when it was opened in 1985.

TUNNELS

The relatively gentle nature of the landscape has required very few tunnels in East Anglia. Those at Audley End and Littlebury on the Eastern Counties Railway Newport-Brandon line have ornate portals, testimony to the fact that the tunnels were required to screen the railway from the view of Lord Braybrooke at Audley End. It is interesting to note that he was prepared to allow the railway to pass on this condition. Earlier in the century the previous lord had successfully blocked any proposal to build a canal from the River Stort to the River Ouse along the same line.

The other major railway tunnel in the region was that at Ipswich, built under the direction of Peter Bruff for the Ipswich & Bury Railway. This one was more difficult to build. The Eastern Union Railway's original station was south-east of the present one, so in order to continue the line round the town to the north it was necessary to set out the line on a fairly tight curve. Of only medium length, at 361 yards, Bruff elected to build three intermediate shafts during construction, which must have mitigated any errors in alignment as well as speeding up construction. More serious were the problems caused by water in the ground. Although Bruff had claimed earlier that it was a compact dry loamy gravel, in parts it was a fine wet sand and, like Kilsby Tunnel on the London & Birmingham Railway, it was necessary to drain the ground before main construction could start. By January 1846, five months after the start, the water had been overcome and the last brick of the lining was laid on 19 September. Since then major tunnels have only been required for the water transfer scheme from the River Ouse to Suffolk.

HARBOURS

At various times there have been more than one hundred harbours along the coast of East Anglia. Many of these have been little more than mud berths or beach landing places and some have disappeared altogether. Only eight have had the benefit of major civil engineering works to enable them to remain open to significant commercial traffic today.

Wisbech was in earliest times at the confluence of the Rivers Nene and Great Ouse, which then flowed through a wide estuary into the Wash. Within the estuary, whose boundaries were defined by the **Old Sea Bank (N22)**, the channel of the river changed course frequently as it became obstructed by silt brought down or sand washed in by the tide. Despite this, at least from the 11th century, ships, large for the time, were able to berth at quays alongside the river. This trade ceased abruptly in 1260 after a tidal surge wreaked havoc. From about this time, too, the waters of the Ouse found their way to Lynn, where the citizens obtained a charter from the king to secure the river in its new course. The construction of **Morton's Leam (C18)** from 1480 restored a better flow of the River Nene to the town and the port was re-established. Despite continuing problems with both river and tidal floods, the port continued; dredging of the channel at least from 1635 maintained the head of the estuary within two miles below the town.

The story of Wisbech as a port from this time on is intimately involved with further reclamation of the marshes below the town and the creation of new channels for the river. The latter were driven largely by the need to drain the North Level of the Fens and were regularly opposed by the corporation of Wisbech, fearful that an already difficult navigation might be harmed rather than improved. The 50 years around the turn of the 18th century saw the port prosper, and the river had been narrowed and embanked for a further two miles down to a place called River's End, but it was a winding course and the flow was not sufficient to prevent another build up of silt. Indeed, below there the channel could move its course laterally by as much as a mile in the space of a year. Foul Anchor (TF 4617) became the point of transhipment from sea-going vessels to barges. In 1722 an attempt was made to restore the channel to flow past Gunthorpe Sluice, the main outlet for the drainage of the North Level, but rioters from Wisbech, afraid as usual of the effects of change, destroyed the works and it was not until 1773 that Kinderley's Cut was made. Despite its success, reluctance to provide finance delayed any further improvements until the 1830s, when the **Nene Outfall (L1)** and Woodhouse Marsh Cut were completed, creating the river much as it is today.

The railway era saw new wharves on each bank of the river, on the east side by the East Anglian, later Great Eastern, Railway and on the west by the Peterborough, Wisbech & Sutton Bridge, later Midland & Great Northern Joint Railway. Each of these proposed wet docks, either on land above the Horseshoe Bend or by cutting a new channel past it on the east and turning the old course into a dock. The final scheme was put forward in 1884, but nothing came of any of them. In the 20th century the old timber wharves have gradually been replaced by sheet piling and concrete, and most traffic is handled on the East Quay.

Sutton Bridge Dock (further down the River Nene, but in Lincolnshire) was an altogether less successful scheme. Designed by Sir James Brunlees, an eminent engineer who had already constructed the Alexandra Dock at King's Lynn and the Queen's Dock at Whitehaven, it was opened on 14 May 1881. The dock was built in quick silt and by the next day it was clear that there was a leak through the ground beside the lock. On 9 June a large hole about 12ft deep appeared on the north side and another to the

27

south; three days later the west wall of the dock had collapsed. An Act of Parliament was passed the following year to raise £160,000 to repair the dock (it had cost £156,000 to build), but the money was not forthcoming and it was never rebuilt. Subsequently the dock was filled in and is now part of a golf course. A reverse bend in the riverside road (TF 483217) still marks the site of the entrance lock; the western girder of the swing bridge that spanned it remains *in situ*. Port Sutton Bridge is a modern venture, with wharves on the river rather than a dock.

King's Lynn in the 12th century was the principal port of the east coast of England between the Humber and the Thames, and in the 14th century was the 12th largest town in England, a fact that it owed largely to its flourishing trade. Originally the ships berthed on the mud flats on the banks of the river but, as the town expanded, timber wharves reclaimed land from the river on which warehouses were built. A fine survivor is the one in St Margaret's Lane, built for the Hanseatic League in the 15th century. Although the diversion of the waters of the Great Ouse past Lynn in the 13th century had helped to keep the river open, further encroachment by groynes and wharves on the east bank and land reclamation

30 *Hanseatic warehouse, King's Lynn. The river is at the far end.*

on the west bank failed to prevent the accretion of sandbanks below the town. Until the 19th century no real development took place, and the Corporation engaged in almost continual dispute with the drainage authorities upstream for fear that new schemes might damage the navigation past the town and into the Wash. That these fears were groundless was shown by the creation in 1818-21 of the **Eau Brink Cut (N25)**, which increased the depth of water at the town for a time. Further proposals to improve both drainage and navigation led to the **Victoria County/Norfolk Estuary (N14)** proposals of 1837. The scheme received its Act in 1846 but was so emasculated in Parliament that only part of the scheme was executed. King's Lynn benefited, however, by the creation of the new straight embanked channel through the Vinegar Sands.

The impetus for the first wet dock in the town (**N13**) (in East Anglia, only Ipswich already had one) came from promoters of local railways that would eventually merge to become the **Midland & Great Northern Joint Railway (N15)**, an interloper in an area where the Great Eastern Railway dominated. The position of the dock had been suggested in 1767 by John Smeaton, one of the many eminent engineers consulted by the town over the years, and it was built in 1866-9 to the designs of (Sir) James Brunlees and (Sir) George Barclay Bruce. The Alexandra Dock was so successful that in 1876 John Valentine drew up plans for another wet dock, leading off the old one to the north east. This, the Bentinck Dock, was constructed in 1881-3. Valentine entered into a dispute with the dock company about his fees for the work, which was settled by the Official Referee awarding some points to each side, but it did not harm his relations with them as he later became chairman of the company. Both docks are still active, in much of their original state.

Norwich, a main commercial centre of East Anglia, is 20 miles from the sea at Great Yarmouth, which for much of recorded history has served as the port of entry for its inland neighbour. Norwich has been a river port for much of that time, though for a short time in the 1830s it, too, became a port of entry. This came about after dissatisfaction with the traditional navigation through Yarmouth led to the construction of the **Norwich**

& Lowestoft Navigation (N10). It was finally opened in 1833 and in the same year an Act was passed creating the Port of Norwich, stretching from the tidal limit at New Mills in the city down as far as Cantley. As at Wisbech, there was a proposal for a wet dock at Norwich, with a lock below Foundry Bridge. This, too, came to nothing and the trade of Norwich continued to be conducted from riverside wharves.

The coast of Norfolk and Suffolk has always been subject to littoral drift – the movement of sand or shingle carried along the coast by the tides. Great Yarmouth is on the site of what was in ancient times the estuary of the rivers Yare and Waveney, but from some time between A.D. 500 and 1000 the drift caused a sandbank to develop. The town built on it was small but of sufficient importance to receive a charter in 1209. The first channel to the sea was north of the town, but the drift blocked it and in 1346 a new entrance was cut, at Corton, six miles to the south. This lasted for only 26 years and this time, in 1393, a channel just south of the walled town was dug. Four more attempts, each in a different place, proved ultimately unsuccessful. The final attempt was made in March 1559, when almost the entire population, men, women and children, worked for three days to cut through opposite Gorleston cliffs. A wooden barrier backed by rubble stone diverted the river through the new gap, which it was hoped would be scoured out further by the ebbing of the tide from Breydon Water. Work continued slowly, hampered by the need for funding, with the advice of an expert from the Netherlands. Work started on a pier, but in 1566 another Dutchman, Joas Johnson or Jansen, was brought over. Under his direction two timber piers, one each side of the entrance and giving a width of 114 yards, were built out, 235 yards long on the north and 340 yards on the south. A timber groyne 500 yards further north impeded the littoral drift and caused a build-up of ground along the shore. Johnson left probably in 1575 and the works continued until 1613; they preserved Yarmouth's status as the third or fourth largest port in England for much of the following century.

In the 18th century varying patterns of trade led to the creation of quays along much of the eastern bank by the old town walls, and later along the west bank too. The emergence of a shingle bar at the entrance led to attempts to divert the ebbing tide along the north pier, with little success, and the commissioners employed a horse-powered bucket ladder dredger to keep the channel open. The south pier had been rebuilt in the 1750s but by 1798 was falling into disrepair. William Jessop, the leading civil engineer of the day, reported on its reconstruction and improvements to the harbour and an Act was obtained the following year; it was done in 1800-6 at a cost of about £18,000. In 1800 he also recommended the construction of a wet dock on Gorleston Marsh but

31 *Great Yarmouth south pier in use, though not as its engineer intended.*

commercial rivalry (Gorleston was then in Suffolk) as well as the projected cost prevented any action. The entrance was still giving trouble in 1818 when, with Jessop dead, John Rennie made a report. The 19th century saw the provision of more wharves, more or less along the whole length of the river on both banks. Existing wharves were reconstructed piecemeal, at first with new timber piles outside the line of the old, and subsequently with steel sheet piling capped by concrete.

Lowestoft in medieval times was subject to the littoral drift that caused so many problems at Great Yarmouth, but its prosperous fishing industry was conducted mostly from the beach and so was little affected. Navigation beacons were established in

1609 to mark the channel in to the Roads where the fish were landed, replaced in 1676 by the first true lighthouse to be built in Britain since the Roman age. The High Light then was a round tower 40ft high, but it was replaced by the present structure in 1874.

The first harbour works at Lowestoft were the result of Norwich's demand for an outlet to the sea independent of Great Yarmouth (see above). In Lowestoft itself there was a sea lock that led down to two piers 500ft long, built to channel the outflow from Lake Lothing to the sea. Of cast iron to a design by (Sir) William Cubitt, a local engineer who became President of the Institution of Civil Engineers, they were completed in 1832 and acted as groynes to arrest the drift of sand along the coast from the north.

32 *Great Yarmouth south pier.*

The Navigation was not a success, and having obtained a loan from the Exchequer Loan Commissioners they were unable to repay, the company was taken over by the commissioners in 1835. After lying more or less derelict for seven years, a group of local men purchased the works but were unable to make them profitable, and were bought out in 1844 by (Sir) Samuel Morton Peto, a railway contractor who had amassed a considerable fortune. Unlike Yarmouth, which depended on its inland waterways for trade, Lowestoft was made by its railways. Having obtained an Act to build a line from Reedham and improve the harbour, Peto and his partner Thomas Grissell moved at speed. The works were designed by Robert Stephenson and George Parker Bidder, who had already been involved with the Norfolk Railway, and included a new 20-acre harbour, extending the existing north pier and enclosing the south one. By 1850 over £200,000 had been spent. As well as work on the harbour and railway, Peto, by now having split from Grissell, created a new town south of the harbour with an esplanade and hotel to match. He also founded the North of Europe Steam Navigation Company to trade with Denmark but this proved unprofitable. The harbour was taken over by the Norfolk Railway and continued to expand – a graving dock designed by Charles Cheffins in 1854 was rebuilt in 1928, renovated in 1971 and is currently used to repair trawlers. The Waveney Dock was built in 1878-3 on land that had been part of the beach 50 years earlier. The trawler basin was extended westwards in 1892-3 and the Hamilton Dock, northwards from the Waveney, in 1902-3. Problems with littoral drift continued and a

33 *Great Yarmouth piers.*

north groyne designed to prevent it was itself swept away twice; the present one was built in 1928-9.

Ipswich is a classic 'head of navigation' port, situated at the lowest point where the River Gipping was bridged, and was important as a port by the 10th century. In medieval times there were a number of quays alongside the river below Stoke Bridge, where wool from the rich hinterland could be loaded for export. By the 1690s the port was obviously in decline, and by 1750 improvements at Great Yarmouth had drained traffic away almost entirely. In 1793 some small revival

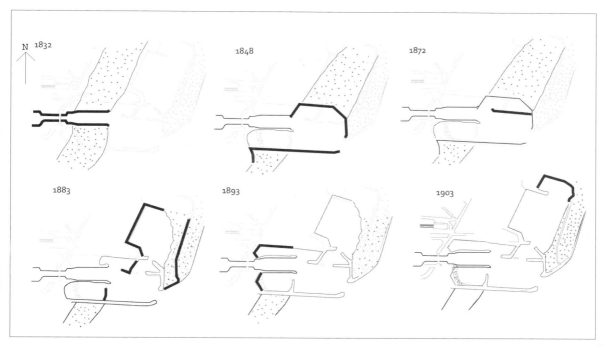

34 *The development of Lowestoft Harbour to 1903. The original seashore embraced the 1832 piers. Dotted areas indicate sand.*

was prompted by the opening of the **Ipswich & Stowmarket Navigation (S10)** which locked into the Orwell at Handford Bridge.

The Orwell by then had become almost impassable at neap tides and some local merchants obtained reports from the leading civil engineer, William Chapman, in 1797 and 1803, from which an Act was obtained in 1805. The work was carried out in 1806-8 and included a 550-yard cut from the shipyard to Cliff Reach, widening and deepening of the river channel to Ipswich Quays and new cuts at Hearth Point and Round Ouze. The deepening was carried out by an early steam-powered bucket-ladder dredger that he had proposed in his 1797 report, which would have been the first such machine had it been built then. In the event it was built to his design with a 6hp engine from Boulton & Watt and machinery from the Butterley Company, and carried out its first trial on 21 July 1806; it remained in use until 1838. In 1819 (Sir) William Cubitt was consulted, who recommended making new cuts to straighten the line of the Orwell. A new channel was cut from the upper end of Lime Kiln Reach to the lower end of Hog Island Reach in 1821.

In 1836 Henry Robinson Palmer, who had worked on the London Docks and been one of the founders of the Institution of Civil Engineers, was consulted about building a non-tidal dock. His solution was ingenious and unusual, though a similar scheme had been built at Bristol 30 years earlier: a new cut would be excavated, cutting off the bend in the Orwell below Stoke Bridge, and the old channel converted into the desired wet dock. An Act was obtained in 1837 and the work carried out in 1838-42; Palmer was Engineer during this time. The cost of the works was about £55,000. His resident engineer, George Hurwood, then took over and further improved the river. The entrance lock was replaced on a new site more in line with the river approach in 1879-81. Built by Henry Lee & Son, a London company who had already dredged the Harwich channel in 1846-51, it cost £45,000.

Felixstowe today claims that one third of all imports into the United Kingdom pass through it. Its history as a port goes back only to 1875, when Colonel George Tomline formed the Felixstowe Railway & Pier Company to develop land that he owned. He obtained a further Act the following year for the excavation of a tidal dock, but only a wooden pier was built then. A third Act in 1879 led to the creation of the dock in 1881-4, with timber lead-in piers each side of an entrance 140ft wide. Though it did not fulfil its founder's vision entirely, the port was a reasonable success in peacetime and served as a naval base in the two world wars. By 1951, when it was taken over by Gordon Parker, it had been eclipsed by developments in other ports. Despite major damage from the floods of 1953, Parker developed new facilities including a freightliner terminal and roll-on/roll-off piers, but the provision of container handling quays since 1968 has been the main engine of growth. The original dock and the ro/ro facility remained, though little used, until 2009, when a massive new development expanded the container berths into deeper water, capable of handling the largest cargo ships afloat.

Harwich, also situated at the mouth of the Orwell estuary but on a direct line from London to the Netherlands and northern Europe, was in medieval times the port of choice for travellers between those parts. The first small harbour was constructed for military purposes by the Crown in 1543 but that was removed in 1657 when the Dutch War of 1652-4 emphasised the value of Harwich as a naval base, and a new State dockyard was built. Further rebuilding took place several times over the next 200 years, sometimes as a result of storms, sometimes to improve the facilities. Like other East Anglian ports, Harwich was subject to littoral drift, but obtained some protection from a stony promontory at Beacon Cliff. A breakwater to divert the flow was proposed by the military engineer Justly Watson in 1754 but it was only when the promontory was quarried in the 19th century for materials in the manufacture of Roman cement that work became imperative. The existing breakwater, or groyne, 1,550ft long, was built from 1846 under James Walker. Originally intended to be almost twice as long, work stopped in 1852 when it became apparent that it was not having the desired effect; only when a corresponding groyne on the Felixstowe side (TM 282312) was built did the two act together to drive Landguard Point back eastward and provide a stable channel into the port.

In 1836 the continental mail service, which had run from Harwich to Hellevoetsluis since 1661, was removed to Dover. This, together with the opening of the wet dock at Ipswich further up the Orwell, and a reluctance in the local marine community to become involved in the new ships that were then making an appearance, led to a decline in the fortunes of Harwich, which were only revived when the Eastern Union Railway constructed a branch from Manningtree to the harbour. The railway had been authorised in 1847 but only opened in 1854; meanwhile an Act had been obtained to permit the upgrading of the port facilities and a new pier. In 1863 the harbour was taken over by the Harwich Conservancy Board, which included members from the Harwich Corporation and the Great Eastern Railway, successor to the Eastern Union, and Peter Bruff was appointed Engineer, a post he would hold until 1895.

Because of opposition from other east coast ports, the railway company had not been allowed to operate its own ship services, until an Act of 28 July 1863 at last permitted it to do so. Almost

35 *Effects of Landguard groyne on the shoreline.*

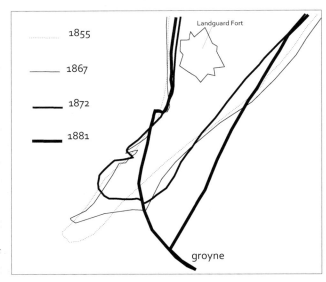

Landguard Fort

.... 1855

———— 1867

━━━━ 1872

━━━ 1881

groyne

36 *Harwich train ferry berth.*

immediately the company laid on services to Rotterdam and in 1864 to Antwerp. Despite its involvement in the Conservancy Board, the company was unable to persuade its colleagues there to provide improved facilities for the new ships it was building, so it decided to create its own port outside the jurisdiction of the Board. Constructed in 1879-83, it was called Parkeston, after the chairman of the railway company, Charles Parkes.

The London & North Eastern Railway, into which the Great Eastern had been grouped, inaugurated a train ferry service from Harwich to Zeebrugge in 1924. There had been a service across the Scottish firths before the Tay and Forth Bridges were built, and more recently there had been several inaugurated on the Continent, but this was the first commercial example in 20th-century Britain. The structure that still stands, disused, at Harwich (TM 258327) was built initially at Richborough in Kent in 1917 to supply the troops in France during the First World War, and was dismantled and re-erected here in 1923-4.

NB: Although Tilbury is in Essex, its history is so much part of London docks that it will be considered in the London volume in this series.

Minor ports

The history of Brancaster, Wells-next-the-Sea, Blakeney and the other ports along the north Norfolk coast show what can happen if there is not sufficient trade to afford the cost of dealing with littoral drift and silting. Records of a port at Wells exist from 1275, and an Act for improvement was passed in 1675. However, the strong tidal scour that kept the tortuous entrance open was diminished by a series of embankments in the 18th century to reclaim marshland formerly covered at high tide. In 1782-3 the most eminent civil engineers in the country, including John Smeaton and Robert Mylne,

37 *Blakeney Quay about 1900.*

were witnesses in a court case to have the embankments removed. Subsequently it became necessary to employ dredgers to keep the port open, at least until 1859 when a straight embankment along the west side of the harbour concentrated the flow of water. Small coasters still come occasionally to tie up at the quay, built with Yorkshire stone in 1846, but the main use is by yachts. Of the other ports there is little to be seen, and no commercial traffic.

Southwold has suffered the same problems and arguments as Wells. Originally the harbour entrance was much further south, near Dunwich, but the present entrance was cut c.1630. From 1700 embankment of areas of the large tidal lake above the town reduced the scour at the entrance, and despite the construction of timber piers north and south in 1749 and 1752 it was necessary no less than 16 times between 1786 and 1830 to dig out the accumulated bar at the harbour mouth. John Rennie senior, in a report dated 6 January 1820, gave it as his opinion that nothing could be done to improve the harbour, and so it has proved. He did, however, propose measures to prevent further deterioration, some of which were later carried out. In 1906 the harbour was bought by a contractor, who built new longer piers curving to the south to give protection against onshore gales, but soon the movement of material along the coast spilled round the end of the north pier, and dredging was necessary again. In 1939 new piers reversed the situation, with a bell-mouth allowing strong flood-tides to scour the harbour, but this has exposed it once more to rough water at the quays.

Mistley, near the tidal limit of the Stour, was unusual in being the creation of two developers, father and son, in the 18th century. A new quay 399ft long was built, as well as a 'new town' to the design of Robert Adam.

Colchester is unlike the ports further north in that its channel to the sea, the River Colne, has tended to deepen rather than the reverse. In medieval times goods were trans-shipped at Wivenhoe, but from the end of the 17th century Colchester Corporation improved the river and quays at The Hythe. In the 19th century the harbour was just one of the responsibilities of the town's improvement commissioners, who had other priorities for the limited funds at their disposal, and an 1842 scheme by Peter Bruff for a ship canal between The Hythe and Wivenhoe did not materialise.

Maldon is another ancient port whose trade has been stunted by lack of civil engineering works. Despite opposition from the merchants, it was bypassed by the construction of the **Chelmer & Blackwater Navigation (E2)** to designs by John Rennie in 1793-7, whose harbour is at Heybridge. Construction of a dock abutting Maldon East

38 *Old quay, Beaumont-cum-Moze.*

39 *Hunstanton Pier (demolished).*

railway station was never completed; part has been filled in, but a derelict water-filled area still remains. Wharves at Fullbridge, on the other side of the river from the ancient quays, called The Hythe like those at Colchester, have allowed some timber import business, but the unimproved state of the river to the town has limited its growth.

Possibly the smallest port, as opposed to a simple landing beach, is Beaumont Quay at Beaumont-cum-Moze (TM 190241), south of Harwich. An artificial cut at the head of a tidal creek is walled with stone for a short length. An inscribed stone, probably from a demolished building, inside the only surviving building (though there is also a limekiln, a rare survival hereabouts) records that that it was erected in 1832 for the Governors of Guy's Hospital. The stone for the quay came from old London Bridge, which was being demolished that year.

PIERS

Several seaside resorts grew up along the east coast of England. A total of 11 seaside piers were built on this stretch of the coast, which faces the North Sea, and only two have failed to survive until the present day: Aldeburgh was 561ft long, built in 1876-8 to the designs

40 *Clacton Pier, c.1900.*

of Thomas Cargill by the contractor G.W. Hutchinson; Hunstanton (TF 671409), built in 1870-1 to the designs of Joseph William Wilson (and similar to his pier at Westward Ho! in Devon), was the outstanding seaside pier of East Anglia, being tall and graceful, though regrettably destroyed during a storm in 1978. A wooden pier that was intended for passengers as well as freight but never developed into a resort was opened at Tollesbury in 1907. It was part of a scheme that included the Kelvedon & Tollesbury Light Railway, the 'Crab and Winkle line', but the promoters' hopes were not realised and the pier closed in 1921; the railway struggled on until 1962.

The remaining seaside piers on this length of the east coast of England are (in order, south to north): **Southend-on-Sea (E10)**, only the fourth seaside pier to be built, having been constructed entirely in timber in 1829-30 and rebuilt in iron in 1887-8. Its ultimate length of 7,080ft makes it the longest in the world. **Clacton-on-Sea (E4)** was originally built in 1870-1 to a design in timber with concrete piles by Peter Bruff, the Engineer of Harwich Harbour as noted above. It was extended in 1890-3 to a design by Walter Kinipple, an engineer who held many patents for marine works. **Walton-on-Naze (E13)**, the fifth seaside pier, when first built in 1830 was only 300ft long, but was demolished c.1895 following severe storm damage and replaced with a longer pier with concrete piles and beams. Peter Bruff was involved here, too, as the major landowner and developer of the seaside resort. Felixstowe (TM 300341) was built in 1905 with a large amusements arcade at the landward end. Southwold (TM 512767) was built in 1900 and rebuilt a century later with single-storey buildings along the deck; structurally it is now one of the least cluttered with bracing. Claremont Pier, Lowestoft (TM 545919), built in 1902, has been truncated, with its facilities at the shoreward end; beyond them, the pier has been closed off. Wellington Pier, Great Yarmouth (TG 531067), the seventh seaside pier, originally built in timber in 1853-4, is another that was heavily rebuilt about the turn of the 20th century, when steel girders were used to support a wider deck for the construction of a theatre. Britannia Pier, Great Yarmouth (TG 531077), was built in timber in 1857-8 and partly rebuilt in steel in 1900-2. Cromer (TG 219424) was the second pier in the country, after Ryde on the Isle of Wight, when it was first built in 1821-2. It was destroyed in a storm in 1843 and rebuilt soon after; the present structure dates from 1900-1 and is relatively short and wide. Despite storm damage it has been well maintained and is in good condition.

LIGHTHOUSES

Although East Anglia possesses no great rock lighthouse like Eddystone or Bell Rock, there is plenty of interest to be seen.

The only substantial remains of a Roman lighthouse in Britain are at Dover, but in the medieval period over 30 lights in church towers or other prominent sites visible from the sea are known by firm evidence or tradition, almost all around the east and south coasts. In East Anglia they are known to have existed then at Great Yarmouth and Orfordness, and probably at Hunstanton, Blakeney and Cromer. St Edmund's

41   An early view of Clacton Pier.

42   Southwold Pier.

43   Groyne under construction, Lowestoft. The message on the card reads 'Have been watching the steamers go off this morning on the pier'.

44   Cromer Pier.

Chapel at Hunstanton was built in 1272 and was said to have had a light tended by a hermit. Some remains still exist near the disused lighthouse built in 1838-40. At Blakeney the light was shown from the great west tower of the church, but the smaller chancel tower, which is sometimes said to have had a light also or to have been built to align with the channel into the harbour, was probably built to distinguish this church from its neighbours as a daymark.

From the end of the 16th century, private individuals petitioned the Crown for patents to build lighthouses and the right to charge dues from passing shipping. In 1609 Trinity House, which had been established by a charter in 1514 and gained the right to provide lighthouses and lightships by an Act of 1566, built its own first lighthouses on the foreshore at Lowestoft.

At Winterton, Norfolk, in 1616 there was in effect a competition between Trinity House and two entrepreneurs for the right to build, with the Crown seeking to turn the situation to its own advantage. With conflicting advice from the highest legal authorities, Trinity House was given permission and did indeed build a tower, but the grant was overturned and awarded to their opponents. They built their own tower in 1618, having used Trinity House's structure in the meantime. A replacement was built in 1677, but no trace exists of these towers. The present one was built in 1840, and was taken out of use in 1921.

45 *Hunstanton Lighthouse, seen through the remains of St Edmund's Chapel.*

Another early pair of lights was that at Hunstanton, built privately under a patent granted in 1665. After one was burnt down, a replacement timber structure was built by Ezekiel Walker of King's Lynn in 1777-8, with an oil lamp instead of a coal brazier, set precisely at the focal point of a reflector and therefore with the light beam focussed. Walker is sometimes credited wrongly with the invention of the parabolic reflector – though he is known to have made improvements in it – but the fame of his Hunstanton Lighthouse was such that the first Engineer to the Commission for Northern Lights was sent to him at King's Lynn to be trained. Hunstanton was one of those whose lease was renewed against the wishes of Trinity House, who purchased it compulsorily in 1837. The existing building was rebuilt in brick during 1838-40 and operated until light ships in the Wash rendered it redundant; it was discontinued in 1921. At both Winterton and Hunstanton the lantern was removed and replaced by an additional storey during conversion to private houses; the lantern from Winterton was taken for re-use in Bombay. Hunstanton is now a holiday cottage.

Cromer (or Foulness) was one of five lighthouses built under a patent obtained in 1669 by Sir John Clayton and George Blake (the others were at Farne Islands, Flamborough Head and two at Corton). Only the last two were lit, but the dues were to be paid voluntarily and insufficient revenue was obtained to keep even them lit; they were extinguished by 1678. A new patent was obtained in 1719 by the landowner, with

46 *Cromer Lighthouse.*

47 *Happisburgh Lighthouse.*

compulsory dues this time levied on passing ships. By the terms of the patent, ownership passed to Trinity House in 1792, who fitted only their second flashing light there: Argand oil lamps with five reflectors on a revolving frame. Cliff slips occurred in 1799, 1825 and 1852 and finally took the lighthouse away in 1866. Foreseeing this outcome, the present lighthouse was built in 1833 on a site a little further inland. It was turned over to automatic operation in 1990 and the keepers' cottages can be rented as holiday accommodation.

Happisburgh is the oldest remaining working lighthouse in East Anglia. Following a tragic winter storm in 1789, when 70 vessels and 600 men were lost off the Norfolk coast, two lights, a high and a low, were erected to form leading lights past the treacherous Haisborough Sands into safe water. They were designed by Richard Norris and William Wilkins senior and commissioned in 1791. In 1863 a new lantern was installed with diagonal frames crossing each other at a constant angle, giving extra strength to the windows and allowing the light to be seen from any position on the sea. This was an innovation sponsored by (Sir) James Douglass, who had only just been appointed Chief Engineer to Trinity House, so Happisburgh must have been one of the first so fitted. The low light was replaced by a lightship in 1883 and demolished soon after, and the high light painted with three broad red bands to distinguish it from Winterton. The keepers' cottages were sold in 1929 when acetylene had been installed and keepers were no longer required; the light has been electric since 1947. Considered redundant by Trinity House in 1988, it was taken over by the Friends of Happisburgh Lighthouse in April 1990 and as such is the only privately operated lighthouse in the UK.

Gorleston was built on a cramped site in the town in 1877-8, which may account for its unusual slimness. The lantern is now disused, but a flashing light in a first-floor window acts with another on a metal pole on the edge of the promenade as leading lights. There are also lights on the roof of the rather utilitarian Coastwatch building at the end of the south pier.

Lowestoft is generally accepted as being the site of the first lighthouse actually built by Trinity House, in 1609, although not on the present site. A pair of candle-lit lights guided vessels through the Stamford Channel into the town. They were rebuilt in 1628 and again in 1676, when the High Light was removed to its present site as the

Stamford Channel had disappeared. This had an open fire, but it was later enclosed because of the fire risk to the town. There must have been a risk to the structure too, as it was still wooden in the early 18th century. The Low Light was built in 1832 to a design of Richard Suter, a pupil of Daniel Alexander, but replaced in 1867 by a movable structure on iron legs built further south on the North Denes. It was discontinued in 1923. The present High Light was rebuilt in 1874 when it was converted to electrical operation. Lowestoft South Pier and North Pier Lights were built in 1847 as part of Peto's development of the port. There is a covered apron and seating at the base; from a distance they look like bandstands.

Pakefield Lighthouse was built in 1832 by Richard Suter. It was replaced after a short time by one at Kessingland because of changes in the channel it was supposed to mark, and was discontinued in 1864. Pakefield is now a Coastwatch Centre, in the Pontin's holiday resort, and no trace remains of the one at Kessingland.

Southwold Lighthouse is a prominent feature in the town itself. Built in 1889-90 to the design of Sir James Douglass, it was the latest of the traditional structures to be built in the region, and replaced three earlier structures that were under threat from erosion. It is open to the public frequently.

48 *Lowestoft South Pier Lighthouse.*

The first lighthouse at Orfordness was built in 1634 for John Meldrum, who had previously been the instigator of the light at Winterton (see above). The structures here were subject to more than their fair share of mishaps. Essentially leading lights to guide vessels through a gap between offshore banks, the low light nearest the shore has been destroyed at least twice by erosion. After the second occasion it was replaced by a moveable timber tower, but this and a successor burnt down, despite having three bushels of rock salt on the floor to provide insulation from the hearth. Finally the present tower was built in 1792-3 to the design of William Wilkins senior, an architect of Norwich, who had been responsible for Happisburgh the previous year. The lighthouse is about halfway down Orford Ness, along which there is no public road, and is accessible by ferry from Orford Quay and more than a mile's walk.

In 1841 a temporary light was fixed on Landguard Fort near Felixstowe, at the entrance to the ports of Harwich and Ipswich. It was replaced by a wooden tower on Landguard Point in 1861, not dissimilar in external appearance from the screw

49 *Harwich Low Lighthouse. The High Lighthouse is behind and to the left of it (also pictured far right).*

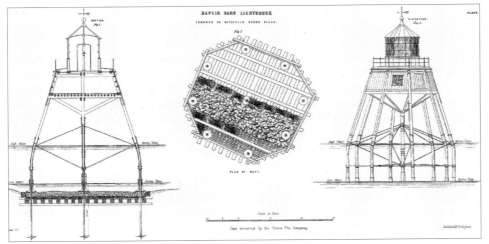

50 *Maplin Sands Lighthouse (Minutes of Proceedings of the Institution of Civil Engineers).*

pile structures (see Maplin, below), but it was burnt down in 1925 and replaced by light buoys.

Harwich Lighthouses (E7) were first built in 1664 as a private venture by Admiral Sir William Batten, the Master of Trinity House. His colleague Samuel Pepys recorded with disapproval that he had used his influence to obtain the patent 'that will turn much to his profit'. They continued to be very profitable to their owner, so much so that the revenue of one year was sufficient to pay for the building of the present lighthouses in 1818.

In 1833 Alexander Mitchell, a blind Irish engineer, obtained a patent for screw piles, intended to anchor moorings to the sea bed. In 1838 nine wrought-iron columns, five inches in diameter with four-foot blades at the ends, were screwed into Maplin Sands, off Foulness Island, to provide the foundation for a lighthouse, the first use anywhere of a method that would make possible the construction of offshore structures on foundations other than hard rock. Because it was then observed that the sand around the piles had changed levels, a timber grating was constructed and sunk onto the seabed under the weight of 120 tons of tough Kentish ragstone, and monitored until it was seen that no further changes were occurring. Thus it was not until the summer of 1840 that the cast-iron columns were placed on top of the piles and a wooden superstructure built. Because of the delay, a similar structure off Fleetwood in Lancashire was the first to be completed, on 6 June 1840; the Maplin light was first exhibited on 10 February 1841. Subsequently many similar lighthouses were built around the world, including three more off the Essex coast. Maplin itself was undermined and swept away in 1932; Chapman (1849) was demolished in 1958 and Mucking (1851) in 1954, leaving only Gunfleet (1850), six miles off Clacton-on-Sea.

51 *Dovercourt.*

Similar structures can be inspected at close quarters at Dovercourt (**E6**). When the channel into the estuary moved and the leading lights at Harwich ceased to be of any use, replacements were built further south in 1862-3. The High Light is on the beach just below the promenade wall and the Low Light, 200m further out, is approached by a causeway at low tide. They were superseded in 1917 and sold to Harwich town council.

POWER

From the earliest times civil engineers were involved in the provision of power, not only in the construction of the groundworks or buildings to house the machinery but also in the power units themselves. This continued well after the Institution of Mechanical Engineers was founded in 1847 and the Society of Telegraph Engineers, forerunner of the Institution of Electrical Engineers, in 1871. Leaders of the civil engineering profession such as John Smeaton and John Rennie received their early training as millwrights. Robert Stephenson and Isambard Brunel both designed the locomotives for the railways that they built, though the former was much more successful in this than the latter. Discussions at the Institution of Civil Engineers on many forms of prime mover continued well into the 20th century. This chapter will concentrate on the more restricted definition of civil and structural engineering that is understood today.

Watermills

Watermills provided the earliest source of mechanical power. There were more than five thousand of them recorded in the Domesday Survey in 1086. They became particularly valuable in the early days of the industrial revolution, towards the end of the 18th century, when improvements in their design and the introduction of cast iron in the machinery they drove made them more efficient, but before steam engines became more economical. Leading civil engineers such as James Brindley (1716-72), John Rennie (1761-1821), William Tierney Clark (1783-1852), Sir William Cubitt (1785-1861) and James Meadows Rendel (1799-1856) trained as millwrights. Thomas Yeoman (1709/10-81) and Joseph Nickalls (d. 1793) were also millwrights and attended the first meeting of the Society of Civil Engineers when it was formed in 1771. Both were involved in navigation schemes in eastern England.

A more local example was William Thorold (1798-1878) who at various times in his career was a farmer, millwright, civil engineer, surveyor and architect. He was awarded two prizes in 1827, one for developing a machine for slicing turnips and the other for an improvement to Captain Manby's life-saving apparatus. He drained Limpenhoe and Southwood under contract of October 1831 for £744; the drainage mill still stands at TG 393019. He was the contractor for the swing bridge over Mutford Lock (1828) and **Acle New Road (N1)** and was surveyor of no fewer than six Norfolk turnpike trusts from the 1830s to 1860s. His enthusiasm for civil engineering was such that his three sons were called John Smeaton, Thomas Telford and William Hazledine.

John Smeaton (1724-92), the leading civil engineer of the 1780s, was probably the first to investigate the provision of water power scientifically, in a career that included nearly 60 new millworks between 1753 and 1791. The power they provided was applied not only to grinding corn or oats, but water pumping, machinery for ironworks, driving rolling and slitting mills, and blowing engines for blast furnaces.

In East Anglia many of the watermills were housed in attractive weatherboarded buildings that have since been converted into desirable residences. However, there are still a few watermills adapted to working museums, where the application of running water to drive machinery can be seen. One of the largest is at Houghton (**C20**) on the River Great Ouse, which had three water wheels and no fewer than ten pairs of millstones. The village of Pakenham in Suffolk is unique in England in having two working mills, though the windmill at TL 931694 is now powered by electricity. Bourne Mill in Colchester (TM 006238) still retains some machinery. Little Cressingham Mill at TF 869002 (restored with help from the Norfolk Buildings Trust but no longer working

52 *St Osyth Tidemill dam.*

53 *Battlesbridge Tidemill.*

54 *Thorrington Tidemill.*

or open to the public) is one of the very few mills that combined wind and water power on one site.

Tidemills

Tidemills are simply watermills driven by water impounded in a reservoir, which is filled from the sea on a rising tide and released through the mill on the ebb. Over time there have been nearly two hundred tidemills around the coast of England and Wales, compared with several thousand mills situated on rivers and streams. To give sufficient fall through the wheel a tidal range of at least 10 to 12ft is desirable and this was available along the coast of East Anglia. The reservoir was normally formed by constructing an embankment across a tidal creek, or by excavating a large pond on the shore and using the earth to embank it to above high-tide level; in each case there would be a sluice that could be closed at the top of the tide. In Essex 27 sites have been identified from documentary evidence (including those along the north bank of the river Thames), and in Suffolk three, though precise location from physical remains is only possible now in a few cases. These include St Osyth (TM 115154), which was so neglected that it fell down in 1962, but had a reservoir of 30 acres, still visible; Fingringhoe (TM 030205), dating from 1531, where the mill building is now converted to housing; Heybridge, near Maldon; Stambridge on the river Roach (TQ 888903), abandoned in 1951 and subsequently burnt down; and Battlesbridge (TQ 780946), where the mill was demolished in 1902 but a modern business can still use the tide pond to power a small generator.

Only three mills in England (plus one in Wales) have their machinery intact. Two are in East Anglia, and of those, **Woodbridge Tidemill (S13)** is working and open regularly to the public. **Thorrington Tidemill (E11)** is not worked at present, but is open to the public occasionally.

Windmills

The East of England is a mecca for molinologists as it has the finest and most diverse collection of windmills in the British Isles. With flat or gently rolling countryside, this is ideal windmill territory.

Cambridgeshire covers part of the Fens, which had a number of corn windmills as well as drainage pumping windmills. A small example survives complete today, now relocated at Wicken Fen (**C36**), and there is another example at Foxton (TL 407483). At Bourn (**C1**) is the oldest surviving open trestle post mill in the British Isles, dated to 1636. There are two other complete open trestle post mills at Great Chishill (TL 414389) and at Great Gransden

55   *Great Chishill Windmill.*

56   *Burwell Windmill.*

43

(TL 277555). Cambridgeshire smock and tower mills were noted for the variety of their caps: ogee caps appeared on half the mills, spread evenly throughout the county; boat-shaped caps were found bordering the Fens; shallow-domed caps without petticoats but with ball finials, and with upright fantail supports braced to the top of the cap, within eight miles of Soham; pepperpot caps in the east of the county. Complete mills can be found at Burwell (TL 590665), with a four-storey tower built of brick and clunch (hard chalk); Haddenham (TL 458745); Over (TL 381688), the most attractive tower mill in the county with ornamental leaded windows; Soham (TL 608717), originally built as a smock mill, with a polygonal tower; and Wicken (TL 571706), which has a two-storey 12-sided black-tarred timber smock on a two-storey tarred tapering circular brick base.

Essex has two complete post mills at Ashdon (TL 595426), a 'head and tail mill' (with one set of millstones in the breast of the buck and another in the tail), and at Aythorpe Roding (TL 590152), originally of the same configuration but later converted into a 'spur gear mill' (with two pairs of millstones in the breast). There are complete tower mills at Stansted Mountfitchet (TL 510248), with a five-storey, 65ft-high brick tower and domed cap, and Thaxted (TL 609308), restored between 1973 and 1997, containing a rural museum.

However, the real glory of this region is to be found in the two eastern counties. Norfolk is renowned for its tall brick tower mills with boat-shaped caps, invented by the Norfolk millwright Dan England of Ludham (1823-97). The Norfolk boat-shaped cap had vertical weatherboarding and a deep petticoat of vertical boards to provide a weather seal between the tower and the cap, which often had a gallery for maintenance access. Most Norfolk tower mills had fantails and four anti-clockwise double-shuttered patent sails. There are many excellent examples remaining, such as the complete tower mills at Billingford (TM 167786), with a five-storey brick tower; Denver (TF 605012), with a five-storey cement-rendered brick tower; Great Bircham (TF 760327), also five-storey, yellow and red brick tower, tarred; Stracey Arms (TG 442090), built in 1883 to drive a turbine for drainage pumping. There is a complete drainage pumping trestle-mounted wind engine at Horning (TG 347163), and a similar wind engine at Ludham (TG 370192), built by Dan England in 1897; both wind engines were restored during the 1980s. A drainage pumping hollow post mill can be found at Ludham (TG 369194), though this was originally sited in the Ranworth Marshes; another is located at Starston (TM 232843), built c.1850; a third is in the

57   *Bircham Windmill.*

58   *Saxtead Green Windmill.*

Upton Marshes (TG 403129). The electricity-generating mast-mounted wind turbine at Swaffham (TF 816099), built in 1999, supplies half the town's electricity needs, and at 318ft high was the tallest in England when it was built.

Suffolk was the most populous county in the British Isles as far as windmills were concerned, with over 700 being recorded in the county, though sadly few remain complete today. It was a county of post mills, which were never superseded by tower mills as in other counties. There were two distinct types of post mill in Suffolk. The turret post mills in West Suffolk were aesthetically very pleasing, many single-storey round-houses having attractive tiled roofs. Some bucks had porches, and fantails were often mounted on the tail ladders. A complete West Suffolk post mill survives at Drinkstone (TL 964622), which bears the date '1689' carved on a beam and has unusual timber framing, as the buck has been turned round head to tail at some date. The mill has clockwise double-shuttered sails, two common plus two spring, the latter fitted with 'skyscraper' air-brakes. Drinkstone is unusual in having two mills side by side, the second a smock mill built to supplement power requirements. For the East Suffolk turret post mills, many 19th-century ones had their roundhouses built at the same time as the bucks, the roundhouses often having two or three floors. Fantails were sometimes mounted on the roofs of the tall bucks. These very tall post mills could be over 45ft high to the ridges of the roofs, and are generally considered to be the finest in the world. The best remaining example is at Saxtead Green (TM 253644), which was in use in 1796, and has been raised three times, now having a three-storey roundhouse (National Trust; open occasionally). Other good examples can be found at Framsden (TM 192598) and Stanton (TL 971733), both with two-storey roundhouses. There is an attractive complete turret hollow post mill at Thorpeness (TM 468598), originally built in 1803 at Aldringham as a corn mill, then moved to this location in 1923 and converted to pump water to the nearby water-tower known as the 'House in the Clouds'. The sole surviving working smock drainage mill in Suffolk can be found at Herringfleet (TM 465976), built c.1820 with an iron-framed scoop wheel with wooden boards. There is a complete tower mill at Thelnetham (TM 011791), with a four-storey tarred tower, and another at Pakenham (TL 931695), considered to be the finest in Suffolk, with a working set of four anti-clockwise double-shuttered patent sails. There is a complete mast-mounted wind engine for water supply at Knodishall (TM 436610).

WATER SUPPLY

The basic components of a public water supply today are a source of raw water, a means of treating it to potable standards, a storage facility to hold sufficient water to maintain a full-time supply while ironing out fluctuations in demand, and a network of pipes to distribute it to the consumers. The provision of a modern mains system has been relatively recent in some parts of the region. It was only in the 1840s that pipe fittings were designed and manufactured to be sufficiently strong for a continuous supply; previously, householders would have to fill a tank in the house during a few hours each day and wait until next day to replenish what they had used meantime. In 1880, Colchester, for instance, still had an intermittent supply. Mains supply in the countryside came late – in Huntingdonshire in 1933 only two of the three boroughs and two of the three urban districts had a mains supply; none of the rural districts did so.

In medieval times, several towns in England had a supply from a remote source, brought to the town by a pipeline. These were usually installed at the initiative of a religious establishment, though there were also examples of private charity by wealthy townspeople. At Cambridge, **Trinity College Conduit (C10)** was made by the Franciscan friars. A 15th-century conduit house stands in Common Plain in the centre of Little

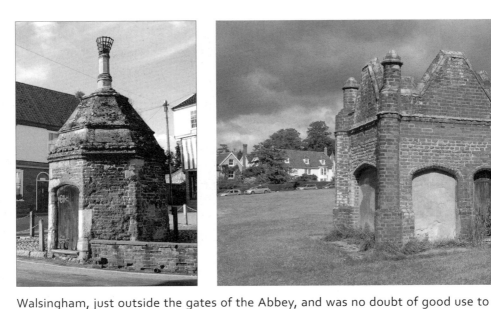

Walsingham, just outside the gates of the Abbey, and was no doubt of good use to the pilgrims who came there. The one at Long Melford is 16th-century (TL 866464). In Norwich, a well a short distance away was piped in 1578 to an ornate alcove in the street. It bore a long inscription testifying to the public spirit of Robert Gybson, a brewer who thereby incidentally gained a supply for his own use. The structure has been removed as redevelopment has taken place, and is now in Anchor Quay below Westwick Street. Maldon, too, had a public supply, provided by Thomas Cannock in 1587. The well house, fed by a spring to the south, was rebuilt in 1805 and still exists in a private garden in Beeleigh Road at TL 8460 0732. From it a pipe led to a cistern house with a pump, halfway down Cromwell Hill; the cistern house has gone and the pump was replaced in 1805; in 2009 it was in the middle of a building site. A stone oval plaque now in the town museum, a relic of this site, is inscribed: 'Restored CC Weston Esq 1748'.

At Leigh-on-Sea a conduit led from a spring on top of the cliff to a cistern in the High Street. A new cistern there was opened by voluntary subscription in 1826; a plaque which records its rebuilding ends with the exhortation 'Waste not, want not'. The stone which stood beside the spring, inscribed 'This stone is plased at ye Spring Head belonging to the cundit by desire of the parishioners of Leigh 1712. William Hutton Churchwarden' was removed to the site of the cistern in 1981, and can be seen in a courtyard below the plaque. A more ambitious scheme was **Hobson's Conduit (C9)** in Cambridge, which brought water in an open channel to the town in 1610 and was extended to provide a public supply in 1614.

Both the 14th- and the 17th-century supplies to Cambridge relied on gravity to bring the water from the source to the town. In other towns that was not possible, so some form of pump would be required. Where the source was a well, a pump might be placed directly over it. Wooden pumps have mostly disappeared, though the late 18th-/early 19th-century structure in the Market Place at Mildenhall is a fine specimen. In the early 19th century cast iron became more common and, being more durable than wood, a fair number have survived. At Stebbing there are no fewer than seven remaining. Most pumps are operated by moving a handle up and down, a few by rotating a wheel. Examples of the former include one in Manor Farm Road, Waresley, unusual in being cased in stone; an obelisk of iron in Hall Road, Southminster, cast by John Richmond of Chelmsford in 1832, and another by Ransome's of Ipswich, at Church Lane/Mill Road, Ridgewell. No two

59 (Left) Little Walsingham Conduit.

60 (Above) Long Melford Conduit.

61 *(Above) Leigh on Sea Conduit.*

62 *(Centre) Obelisk at Nine Wells, near Cambridge, source of Hobson's Conduit.*

63 *(Right) Water pump, Mildenhall.*

wheel-operated pumps seem to be identical, and variations can be seen in Main Street, Hardwick; Head Street, Goldhanger (TM 904088); The Street, Steeple and The Bury, St Osyth, made by Bamford of Uttoxeter and possibly intended to be driven by their steam-powered machinery. Possibly the most unusual is the windpump in Pulham Road, Starston, part of a system dating originally from c.1560 to supply Starston Place.

Where the source was a river, it was often necessary to provide a greater pumping power to take the water to a cistern to allow for some form of purification before supply to the public. From the late 16th century this usually took the form of a waterwheel driven by the river from which the water supply was being extracted. The most famous of these were under the arches of London Bridge, the first of which was installed by Peter Morris in 1580-2, and were upgraded by George Sorocold in 1701-2. In East Anglia he and a partner, Richard Barry of Westminster, in 1694 undertook waterworks in Great Yarmouth, and by 1698 Sorocold had almost certainly replaced the windpump of 1682 at King's Lynn by a waterwheel. For his work at London Sorocold became known as 'the great English engineer', almost certainly the first person to be described thus.

Peter Morris was also responsible for the design of the original Norwich Waterworks in the late 16th century. In 1694 Sorocold and Barry signed a 99-year agreement with Norwich Corporation to supply water to the town for £200 and an annual rent of £25. By a separate agreement they acquired a lease of the New Mills, and carried out the works in 1698-1700; their rights were confirmed by an Act of Parliament in the latter year. By 1788 there were problems with the supply and Robert Mylne, the Engineer of the New River which supplied London, was asked to report. He did so in January 1789, recommending that the New Mills be restricted to water supply and grinding corn. An Act was passed in 1790 but progress was slow and the lessees of the mills brought in Joseph Bramah to design new waterworks. His design, the only civil engineering work that he undertook in a distinguished career, was ready in September 1796. Mylne then brought in Boulton &

64 *Water pump, Hardwick.*

47

Watt to comment and Bramah issued a vituperative pamphlet in reply. Bramah probably carried out the work despite Mylne's comments. As a mechanical engineer, Bramah was responsible for the water-powered, three-throw pump that is said to be intact inside the small pumphouse at Little Cressingham. It was built to supply the gardens of Clermont Hall, about a mile away, when that was rebuilt in the early 19th century.

By the 1830s the growth of towns and the associated squalor and epidemic diseases led to attention being given nationally to questions of water supply. The Municipal Corporations Act of 1835 gave local authorities a right to improve public utilities in their area, though this power was only permissive, and by 1848 only 29 councils out of 188 had made use of this. The first attack of cholera in Britain in 1831 was followed by others, in which thousands of people died. The medical evidence showed that the incidence of cholera was closely related to contaminated water supply, though the potential costs caused the water companies to resist removing their intakes to less polluted sites. At much the same time, the problems of sanitation moved up the public agenda, partly due to, partly in spite of, the lawyer/reformer Sir Edwin Chadwick. He pointed out that there could be no improvement in sanitation without liberal amounts of water to take away the sewage of the cities. The Waterworks Clauses Act of 1847 made a constant supply mandatory, though in practice this desirable end was a long time coming in some places. The Public Health Act of 1848 set up a General Board of Health and allowed the election or appointment of local boards. The inspectors appointed under this Act produced 243 reports in the first five years and in 1852 one of the inspectors, (Sir) Robert Rawlinson, presented a paper 'On the Drainage of Towns' to the Institution of Civil Engineers. Until then, sewers had been large enough for a man to enter in order to flush them out. The paper set out the features of a modern sewer system with pipes for local drains, laid in straight lines with manholes at changes of direction, and laid to falls so as to be flushed by flowing water. At the same time John Roe, the Surveyor-in-Chief of the Metropolitan Commission of Sewers, developed the egg-shaped cross-section that made the flushing process much more effective. By 1862 178 authorities had adopted the 1848 Act or its successor of 1858, and £4 million had been loaned for capital improvement works. Because the dreadful mortality rates had markedly reduced as a result, the Sanitary Act of 1866 gave the government power to construct the necessary works and back-charge those local authorities who had not taken action.

65 *Epping Water Tower.*

In the event, action was only enforced in seven places, but Epping was one of them. Joseph Clegg, a local doctor, campaigned from 1853 for better water and sewerage, but in 1867 the death rate was the highest in Essex. He then complained to Home Office under section 49 of the Sanitary Act; his complaint was upheld. A petition for a special drainage district under the Sewage Utilisation Act, 1867, was accepted by the Home Office in 1868 but the local authority refused to act, and resigned. The Home Office then put the works in hand, successfully defending a challenge in the Queen's Bench in 1870. By 1872 an artesian well had been sunk and a water tower built, at a cost of £11,900. Because the well had not produced as much water as expected, the local authority agreed only in 1878 to take over part of the debt. The works were sold to a private company in 1879; then again in 1880 to Edward Easton, who formed the Herts. & Essex Water Co. (now the Lee Valley Water Co.) in 1883. There were still only 392 customers in 1884.

The water tower, designed by the eminent firm of Thomas Hawksley, still stands on the north-west side of Epping High Street at TL 457018.

Colchester, on the other hand, was supplied from early days by a spring in Chiswell Meadow, mentioned in 1536. A pump was maintained by the parishioners of St Peter's in 1659; King Coel's Pump was referred to in 1763, and there was another in Castle Passage in 1804. The Cistern Yard at the bottom of North Hill went out of use at some time between 1768 and 1789. In 1808 the entrepreneurial engineer Ralph Dodd proposed a scheme to improve the supply from Chiswell Meadow. He laid water mains in the streets, to which the householders were required to lay and connect leaden pipes. Contemporary comment was divided on the efficiency of the works, though some of the criticism seems to have been directed at Dodd as an outsider. The springs by 1850 had run low so that the company was no longer able to continue. It was bought by a group that included Peter Bruff, whose first attempt to find a new supply 340ft down in the chalk ended in failure. A second attempt in 1851 breached a fissure of flint in the chalk at -353ft, from which copious quantities came forth. A new spring south of Sheepen Farm supplemented this in 1860. The works were sold to the Corporation in 1880, who proceeded to build the water tower on Balkerne Hill (**E5**). The original springs were no longer considered fresh enough for domestic use and were used to supply water for the locomotives at Colchester North station.

Harwich was another town with an early scheme to provide a public water supply, though in this case with much less success. Under an Act obtained in 1819 for a general improvement of the town, a plan was drawn up by William Scott for (Sir) William Cubitt, but nothing was done about the water supply. When Peter Bruff was constructing the railway to the town in 1854, water was still being obtained from shallow wells or shipped down in barrels from Ipswich or Mistley. He contracted with the town council to provide an adequate supply within two years; if successful, he would be allowed a monopoly for 75 years. His first borehole, beside the Corporation Quay, took four years and went down 1,100ft, without success; Bruff later remarked wryly that it threw a new light on the geology of the district. Although the agreement had lapsed, he tried again at Dovercourt and going down 400/500ft, found slightly salty water in 1865. Further trials within the borough boundary – for the council would have needed another Act of Parliament to go outside – were no more successful and after an abortive attempt to sell his company, in which he had spent over £18,000 of his own money, Bruff obtained statutory authority in 1884 to set up the Tendring Hundred Water Company with works at Mistley and Bradfield.

Almost the reverse occurred in the Brentwood area. The South Essex Waterworks Company was formed in 1861 to sell supplies of water flooding the chalk pits at Grays, which, with an elevated reservoir at Brentwood, were sufficient until 1891 to supply the area from Grays to Barking. The original site has been built over, but an impression can be gained from nearby Chafford Hundred (TQ 599786).

A supply to Chelmsford was mentioned in 1683. It had wooden pipes, leading to a head in Conduit Street, now renamed Tindal Street. About 1769 the original pipes were replaced by lead ones, and the head itself was rebuilt in 1791; it was surmounted by a statue of a woman in classical Greek dress, apparently designed by the architect John Johnson, who was rebuilding the Shire Hall nearby at the same time. The present conduit head, a stone dome on six Doric columns, was the result of an initiative in 1812 by a merchant in the town, Robert Greenwood, whose legacy motivated others to contribute. By 1814 enough had been subscribed for it to be built. It was removed to the lower end of High Street in 1851 and then to Tower Gardens, Roxwell Road in 1940. The original supply was inadequate by the mid-19th century and a Local Board

66 *Grays Waterworks (Illustrated London News).*

67 *Chafford Hundred chalk pits.*

was formed in 1850 under the Public Health Act of 1848. A scheme to have an artesian well near Mildmay Road was proposed in 1852 by James Fenton; it was 361ft deep but provided an inadequate supply. The Borough Waterworks were in use by 1868 and the water tower at Rainsford was proposed in 1888.

At the other end of the region, when Peterborough was incorporated as a municipal borough in 1875, its citizens still relied exclusively on shallow wells for their water. The new authority immediately set about providing an abundant supply as well as a new system of drainage. A borehole 286ft deep was sunk at Castor, five miles to the west, where it was expected that a bed of marlstone similar to that on which Northampton relied would be suitable. The quantities found were quite inadequate so the decision was made to go to Braceborough, a village where there had been a small spa. A site was chosen near a branch railway in order to supply coal to the pumping engines, which raised the water to a service reservoir on nearby Obthorpe Hill, from where it flowed by gravity to the town.

This must have been a poignant contrast to Thorney (**C31**), an estate village of the Dukes of Bedford seven miles east of Peterborough, which had a complete mains supply and sewerage from 1855. Another village with a supply provided by the local patron was Terling near Witham, where c.1868 the 2nd Lord Rayleigh demolished the watermill (TL 771147) on the River Ter that had been built a century earlier by his father and installed a water-driven pump to supply the village from the Swan Pond. A square cast-iron pipe led the intake through a control valve to drive an undershot cast-iron wheel with 24 curved vanes. The supply of drinking water was raised to a cast-iron chest containing three non-return valves, from which it passed through a domed cylindrical collector and a gravity-operated safety valve to a system of standpipes in the village, with an overflow in Wat Hobbs Lane. It remained in use until c.1915.

Other interesting relics of early water systems include the 17th-century well house at Berden, Essex that includes a well more than 120ft deep, over which is a treadwheel. The wheel is 15ft diameter by 3ft 6in wide and is therefore large enough to be worked by a donkey, though it is recorded that it was done by two men. The axle is rectangular and this carried a wooden drum 3ft 4in in diameter on which the rope was wound. It is listed Grade II* and the wheel is still in working order.

Water towers

Water towers serve two purposes: they provide storage to allow for fluctuations in demand, and maintain the pressure in the mains system. Where it is possible to find a site at ground level at a sufficient height above the area to be supplied, that option is usually preferred on grounds of cost, but in East Anglia there are today more than 240 water towers owned by the statutory undertakers.

Probably the earliest water tower to survive is that on the estate of Houghton Hall (**N12**). Dating from the 1730s, it is also one of the most ornate, having been designed by Henry, Lord Herbert. The 1855 tower of the tank yard in the Duke of Bedford's estate village of Thorney (**C31**) rises high above the rest of the village when seen from the recently opened bypass.

Though many Victorian water towers have been replaced as towns have expanded and more villages have been added to the mains supply, there are still several remaining in East Anglia. Probably the best known is the **Balkerne Hill tower (E5)** in Colchester, known as Jumbo, built in 1882-3. It has a cast-iron tank with internal flanged joints. That for the military in Le Cateau Barracks (TL 992246) (1875) in the same town has the flanges externally; the cast-iron plates have diagonal stiffeners which, together with the flanges, add architectural effect to structural necessity. The 1886 tower at Southwold (TM 501763) sits alongside its replacement of 1937. The older tower was most unusual in having its pump in the form of a windmill on the roof of the structure; this has now gone. It was also unusual for a Victorian tower to remain when a replacement was built. East Anglia has two other examples, at East Dereham and Diss. The water tower of 1872 at Epping is a reminder of how troublesome it was on occasion to move the authorities to provide an adequate supply.

Even the great and good were not immune from problems. In 1871 the condition of the water at Sandringham House, which had been bought for the Prince of Wales in 1862 and rebuilt in 1870, was examined by the Rivers Pollution Commission and found to be unfit for human consumption. The existing shallow well was abandoned and a supply led from springs 750 yards away to a tower 60ft high, **Appleton Water Tower (N23)**, a prominent landmark from several directions whose height provided the pressure to carry the water over an intervening ridge.

Some water towers used pre-existing structures. The recently formed Cottenham Gas & Water Company purchased the tower windmill in the village (TL 445675) for £315 in July 1898 and replaced the superstructure with their tank, taking five years over the process. Slightly more common in these days of rationalisation is the conversion of redundant water towers to other uses. This is not always easy to achieve, as the structures by their nature are robust and the tanks watertight. One of the more ambitious examples is that at Wivenhoe (TM 039227), built in 1901 with a cast-iron tank on top of a brick tower, where the tank has been removed and replaced by a glazed living space below the ornate hipped roof and cupola of the old tank. A smaller version, still with the tank intact, can be seen across the river from Wivenhoe at Rowhedge, and

From left to right:

68 *Chelmsford Conduit, re-sited in Tower Park.*

69 *Cottenham Water Tower.*

70 *Soham Water Tower.*

71 *Dovercourt Water Tower.*

72 *Thorpeness Water Tower.*

73 *Raveningham Water Tower (Barry Barton).*

there is another at Lyons Hall Lane, Bocking. The one at Soham was opened as late as 1923.

Metal water towers are rare in Britain. The oldest now remaining is believed to be that at Dovercourt, one of two in the area built in 1902 (TM 243309). The only public supply tower in Britain to have a steel spheroid tank on a single tubular shaft is at Wittering (TF 051025). One of the oddest steel towers in East Anglia is the House in the Clouds at Thorpeness (TM 468598). It was built in 1923 to supply the resort being developed by Glencairn Ogilvie, a younger son who eventually inherited much of the wealth of his father, the railway contractor Alexander Ogilvie, who had settled at Sizewell House. The water tower was disguised by having a weatherboarded house built into it; it had the added attraction of having the water pumped up to the tank by a windmill across the (unmade) road, moved here from Aldringham at the same time. There is a diagram of the works beside the mill and the House is now let as a holiday home.

74 Sapley Water Tower, Huntingdon.

Because reinforced concrete was introduced to Britain shortly before the turn of the 20th century, by which time most towns had a piped supply, concrete water towers are generally to be found in the countryside. Meyrick Park tower at Bournemouth was the first, in 1900, but has now been demolished. Because the apostle of reinforced concrete, Louis Mouchel, does not appear to have had agents in East Anglia, none of the first 49 towers (to 1918) built to his design were in the region. By the 1930s Mouchel had produced standard designs for tanks of different sizes, but other concepts were also appearing. One was the Intze, or balanced, design, developed at Aachen, which aimed to make the base of the tank cheaper to build by dispensing with the beams that would otherwise be needed to support it. The first concrete Intze tank in this country was built near Doncaster in 1923, but the

75 *New Mills, Norwich.*

one of 1933 at Caister-on-Sea (**N4**) has a tank holding 784,000 gallons. It was claimed to be the largest of its type at the time, and is still one of the largest of any type in Britain. Another first in Britain is to be found at Raveningham (TM 413952), though in this case the design originated in Sweden. Here in 1977 the bowl was assembled at ground level from precast concrete units, then jacked up the tower to its final position.

For some less obvious reason prestressed concrete water towers are rare in Britain. The technique requires specialist equipment and higher grade materials than conventional reinforced concrete, but there is a corresponding saving in the quantities of these materials. The advantage of prestressing the reinforcement in water towers is that the tension in the reinforcement is balanced by compression in the concrete, thereby closing up any small cracks that might otherwise occur and preventing minute leaching from damaging the structure. The number of existing structures in this country can probably be counted on the fingers of one hand, but one of them is at Sapley (TL 238741), built in 1963 and now in the middle of an industrial estate on the northern outskirts of Huntingdon.

Because of their height water towers are often notable features in the landscape. The tallest water tower in East Anglia is at Sprites Hall Lane, Trimley (TM 287364), close by the approach road to Felixstowe. It is a reinforced concrete structure with a multitude of columns, built in 1934. Rivey Hill water tower (TL 566478) stands on top of a hill more than 60m above Linton. Although it was built a year after the one at Trimley, its prominent position has meant that it is clad entirely in brick.

Sewerage

The history of sewerage has been mentioned briefly above in the section on water supply, with which in modern times it rightly belongs. One other development which came from the General Board of Health in 1852 was the recommendation that there should be two sets of sewers, one at the backs of houses to take the sewage from the house, and one at the front to take runoff from rainstorms. As with so many ideas of the time, the cost of doing the work was such that uptake was slow, though by the 1880s the principle at least was well established. One obvious disadvantage of water-borne sewage, recognised even by the advocates of reform, was that the easiest way of disposing of it was to let it flow into the most convenient river. For towns on tidal rivers, such as London, the sewage returned twice a day; at others, people downstream had to put up with the pollution. Filtration had been practised at Glasgow and then Lambeth since the 1820s, but the lowest point of a drainage system was not always the most convenient place for filter beds. Pumps to push the sewage to some higher point or some distance away became necessary. At Cambridge, **Cheddars Lane Pumping Station (C2)** was built in 1894-5, using steam power to pump to a sewage farm at Milton, two miles away. In Norwich, the New Mills Pumping Station (TG 226091), mentioned above, was adapted to become a water-powered air compressor that forced the sewage to Trowse.

GAS

Gas was first used for lighting on a large scale by William Murdoch in 1805-06 and the Gas Light & Coke Company, which later amalgamated with others to supply most of London, was founded in 1812. Civil engineers were involved in almost every aspect of gas manufacture, storage and distribution throughout the 19th century. Gasholders needed to be gas-tight, and several different methods were tried to ensure this. They also were large structures, and their design developed to make them lighter and therefore cheaper to construct. An early gasworks was the one at Ipswich, constructed privately at Ransome's works by their engineer, (Sir) William Cubitt. It was sufficiently successful to encourage them to build a public supply in the town in 1821. But the most

76 *Saffron Walden Gasworks.*

77 *Bassingbourn Gasworks.*

prolific designers of gasworks in East Anglia were the father and son, both called Jabez Church. The father was Engineer to the Chelmsford Gas Company from 1846, and his success there led to a career as a consultant, as far afield as Dublin. In East Anglia he was responsible for Colchester (1850s) and with his son, Harwich, Epping, Braintree, Brentwood, Saffron Walden and Cromer (all between 1869 and 1875). They also had a practice in urban drainage and water supply, about which they advised Witham, Epping, Thetford, Clacton, Braintree and Halstead in the 1860s.

By the 1850s most towns and some villages had their own gasworks. The process of making 'town' gas was not very friendly environmentally and when North Sea gas became widely available in the 1970s most gas works were demolished. Some small buildings remain at Bassingbourn (TL 336440). A larger building in Thaxted Road, Saffron Walden (TL 544384) has the legend 'Gas Works 1836' on the road frontage; the site is now a plant hire yard. Norfolk contains the only complete gasworks in England, now a museum, at Fakenham (**N7**). The most usual relics of gasworks are the gasholders, some of which have been retained to provide local storage. A fine example of 1884 remains in Admiralty Road, Great Yarmouth (TG 527061).

LAND DRAINAGE AND SEA DEFENCES

The Fens constitute the largest artificially drained land area in the country. They have been described as the sink of 13 counties, from the catchment area of the rivers that flow into them. To prevent floods from overwhelming them, two problems had to be solved: the upland waters had to be carried over land below the outfall level, and tidal waters had to kept at bay. In earliest times the Wash was much larger than it is today. In the absence of any embankments at its margins its extent would have varied significantly as land and mean tide levels lowered and rose over time. There is evidence of Roman settlement on land that is now below sea level. The limits of the Wash in pre-Conquest times are shown by the **Old Sea Bank (N22)**, a low embankment about 80 miles long that extended continuously from Wainfleet Haven near Skegness to Wiggenhall St Mary near King's Lynn. It was called the Roman Bank by the eminent historian Sir William Dugdale in the 16th century, but he might as well have called it the Devil's Bank for all the evidence of a Roman origin. Bicker, Spalding (both in Lincolnshire) and Wisbech were at the heads of tidal estuaries and Lynn lay beside the estuary of what then was the outlet only of the rivers Little Ouse and Nar. Lack of archaeological or written evidence – the first documentary record dates from 1182 – makes it impossible to ascribe a date for the construction of the Old Sea Bank. It may well have been built by different parishes or groups of parishes at different times. The oldest portions are thought to date from the Saxon period, and it was modified as recently as the late 13th century.

The next major change to the landscape must have been a coordinated effort, probably driven by the burghers of King's Lynn. Until the middle of the 13th century the waters of the River Great Ouse as well as those of the River Nene had reached the sea via Outwell and Wisbech. Silting having blocked the estuary there, these waters had instead been diverted along the Well Creek to King's Lynn. The town now gained royal permission to create a cut from Littleport to Denver, shortening the course of the Ouse and thus improving the scour of the outfall. No further large-scale work in the Fens seems to have been undertaken until John Morton, elected Bishop of Ely in 1479, planned and supervised the 12-mile straight cut for the River Nene from Stanground near Peterborough to Guyhirn that is still known as **Morton's Leam (C18)**. By regaining much of the water that had gone round by the Old River Nene through March and the other channel to the River Welland at Crowland, the outfall at Wisbech was once again navigable by ships.

The wars in the Netherlands in the later 16th century and the two-way contacts it involved aroused interest in draining the Fens, which seemed to be easier to achieve than the existing reclamations in Zeeland and Holland. The first move towards a general draining of the Fens was a survey ordered by the Privy Council in 1589; though nothing came of it at the time, it formed the basis of later schemes. In 1605 Sir John Popham was authorised to drain about 230,000 acres and between August and December a 5½-mile cut was made from the Old River Nene to the Well Creek at Nordelph under the supervision of John Hunt. Storm damage in 1606 and Popham's death in 1607 put an end to the larger scheme, but many of Hunt's proposals were executed in the first major campaign to be completed. This was undertaken for the 4th Earl of Bedford and his 'Co-Adventurers' in 1631-6 and involved works on a scale not seen before. As well as constructing the Seventy-Foot River, now known as the Old Bedford River, the River Welland was improved from Peakirk near Peterborough to its outfall; the New South Eau was constructed from Crowland to Cloughs Cross and the Shire Drain improved from there to Hill's Sluice; the 10-mile Peakirk Drain was made to the River Nene at Guyhirn; Bevill's Leam, also 10 miles long, was dug from Whittlesey to Guyhirn; Sam's Cut, six miles long from Feltwell to the Great Ouse, was made; Morton's Leam was widened, Popham's Eau restored and Well Creek improved; and Wisbech and Hermitage Sluices built on the River Nene and Great Ouse respectively. Although Sir Cornelius Vermuyden was one of several people involved at the planning stage, these works were directed by Andrewes Burrell.

The result of this first campaign was that the Fens were now kept dry during the summer months. After the turmoil of the Civil War, a second campaign was undertaken for the 5th Earl of Bedford to prevent winter flooding and make the land fit for arable farming. Vermuyden was appointed Director of Works in January 1650 and the works were completed in 1656. At their height, 10,000 men were employed. The Hundred-Foot, or New Bedford, River was dug parallel to the Old Bedford River and the land between them provided a reservoir where winter flood waters could be stored until the rivers subsided sufficiently to allow them to drain out to sea. Tidal water was kept out of the South and Middle Levels by the construction of **Denver Sluice (N6)**, a work whose desirability would be the subject of fierce controversy for over a hundred years.

Smaller-scale works continued to be undertaken over the following 300 years. Among the more important was Smith's Leam from Peterborough to Guyhirn. Vermuyden had made a start on banks beside Morton's Leam in 1640-1, but lack of funds meant they were not completed until the 1650s. In 1728-30 a new cut and bank parallel to Morton's Leam created washlands for the River Nene analogous to the Ouse washes mentioned above. The improvement of the outflow of the River Nene had been started in 1722 but forcibly abandoned; **Kinderley's Cut (N24)** was not made until 1773. A river bypass to avoid the narrow channel through Wisbech, often proposed, was never made. The success of this work led, again after lengthy delays, to the **Eau Brink Cut (N25)** on the River Great Ouse. This also provided great benefits to the drainage and the navigation, though they diminished over time and it took the **Norfolk Estuary (N14)** works to restore the situation.

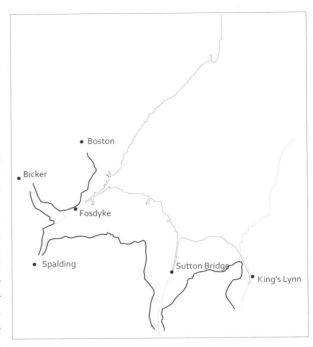

78 *Sea Bank, map.*

79 *Welches Dam, showing the Old Bedford River and the counter drain, joined from the right by the Forty-Foot or Vermuyden's Drain. (Cambridge University Collection of Air Photos)*

80 *Forty-Foot/ Sixteen-Foot Drains.*

The North Level drainage **(C32)** was greatly improved by works undertaken in 1830-4, initially designed by the local engineers Thomas Pear and William Swansborough, though taken through with Thomas Telford as consultant. The **Middle Level (N26)** was similarly dealt with in 1844-52, though the South Level had to wait until the 1960s for the Cut-off Channel round its south-east side, a catchwater drain that had been proposed by Vermuyden in 1639 and Rennie in 1809. In the 1970s the Ely Ouse to Essex Transfer Scheme allowed water to be pumped from Denver along an artificial river and through tunnels to reservoirs at Abberton south of Colchester and Hanningfield south of Chelmsford; the purpose being to supply water to an area where natural resources are inadequate to demand, but it also improved flood control in the Fens.

81 *(Below) Cutting Holme Fen Engine Drain (Illustrated London News, 1851).*

Drainage has created its own problems. Much of the southern Fens is peaty, and as it has dried out the land level has shrunk. First windmills, then steam engines, diesel engines and now electric motors have been required to drive the scoop wheels or pumps that raise the water from local drains into the main rivers. Even these have required adjustment over the years. The Hundred-Foot Engine House (TL 508891) was first erected in 1830, when its scoop wheel was 37ft 5in in diameter, but by 1844 it was necessary to make that 41ft 8in. In 1881 a new 50ft wheel was installed, but since the 1920s the scoop wheel house has been lowered. Another visual indicator of the amount by which the land can sink is shown by the **Holme Fen posts (C19)**.

82 *(Below right) Hundred-Foot Engine House, showing the roof line of the former scoop wheel house above the present structure.*

83 *Turf Fen Mill, Ludham.*

84 *Boardman's Mill, Ludham.*

A glance at any map to a scale of 1:50,000 or larger will show many other areas in the region that have been artificially drained. One of the largest is Halvergate Marshes between the tidal rivers Yare and Bure west of Great Yarmouth. It is particularly notable now for the number of derelict windpumps that formerly emptied the water from the marshes into the rivers. Berney Arms Windmill is the tallest; it was originally used to grind cement, but a later scoop wheel can still be seen on its east side. There is no road to it and the rail station has an infrequent service; access is easiest by boat. Near Ludham the River Ant has an interesting variety of drainage mills within a short distance. Turf Fen Mill (TG 369188) is a tower mill with a Norfolk-type boat-shaped cap, built in the 1870s. Boardman's Mill (TG 370192) is an open-framed timber trestle with a miniature cap, sails, fantail and a turbine. Clayrack Mill (TG 369194) is the only surviving hollow post with its original scoop wheel. It was erected in the mid-19th century on the Ranworth Marshes, and brought here for preservation in 1981. All three can be seen from the footpath that leaves How Hill (TG 372191). For much of its length, the River Waveney is bounded by drainage ditches, which become quite extensive below Burgh St Peter. **Minsmere Level (S12)** is another substantial area, originally draining into the sea near Dunwich, but improved in 1812-14 by William Smith, the 'Father

of Geology'. Opposite Great Yarmouth, the land on which Gorleston Lighthouse now stands was reclaimed in 1813. On the north side of the River Waveney near Somerleyton is **Herringfleet Windmill (S10)**, the last remaining drainage smockmill in working order. The encroachment on the river here probably aided rather than hindered the navigation; the opposite could be true when land was reclaimed from an estuary. If marshes in the estuary were flooded at high tide, the ebb would help to scour the outfall and keep it open for ships. The Blyth estuary in Suffolk was a case in point: 550 acres of land had been embanked anciently, 83 acres south-east of Blythburgh Bridge c.1770 and 166 acres north-east and north-west of it c.1780; Bulchamp New Saltings were added in 1804. Further works in 1807 and 1818 reduced the scour by another 60 per cent. When further enclosures were proposed in 1820, the Blyth Commissioners decided to call a halt; since then Tinkers Marshes and Walberswick Marshes have been reclaimed and narrowed the outfall, but Bulchamp Saltings are once more overflowed and assist the scour.

Similar problems could occur where land was reclaimed from the sea. Land at Holkham was embanked in the late 17th century and in 1719 more land, both east and west of Wells harbour on the Norfolk coast, was inned. The harbour, like

85 *Clayrack Windmill, Ludham.*

86 *Sea defences, Canvey Island.*

61

others nearby, was liable to silt up and in 1778 the Harbour Commissioners resolved to remove an embankment that had been made 20 years before. The result was a series of legal hearings between the landowners and the commissioners that involved the leading engineers of the day. The commissioners won the legal argument at the third and final trial but it was a Pyrrhic victory; a new embankment was built later on a slightly different line and a reservoir that was promised to aid the scour was never constructed. Much the same happened at Cley (**N5**), though at Burnham Norton (**N2**) there does not seem to have been any problem.

Another major, but earlier, reclamation was Canvey Island in Essex. It was initially done c.1622, when an agreement was made between the local landowners and a Dutchman, Joas Croppenburgh, though the work may have been well underway by then – there are two Dutch houses on the island, dated '1618' and '1621', the former now a museum. Here 3,600 acres were reclaimed, of which Croppenburgh's share was one third. The island is embanked all round, and the Thames-side defences were strengthened in the 1930s. An interesting feature from that time is the Labworth Café, designed by Ove Arup as an integral part of the new sea wall; he later was Engineer of the Sydney Opera House.

SEA DEFENCES

Two principal problems have affected the coasts of East Anglia. Littoral drift has tended to move eroded material around the coast, and tidal surges, often allied to strong northerly winds, have overtopped coastal barriers and flooded low-lying land. The littoral drift goes generally anti-clockwise west of Sheringham and clockwise east of there. The principal adverse effects have been the blocking of harbour entrances, and some attempts have been made to reduce its effects by the construction of groynes, some substantial, others in extensive series. The most substantial were at Lowestoft (**S7**) and Felixstowe (see Chapter 3). Harbour entrances were protected by piers, which acted as groynes. At Southwold Harbour, the north side of the north pier is now a beach; the south side of the south pier, which projects as far into the sea as the north pier, has no beach. Piers do help to channel the ebb and flow of the tide, but most harbours along this coast have also required the assistance of dredgers.

The fate of Dunwich in the Middle Ages is well known, but coastal erosion continues today. At Happisburgh several houses have been swept away in the last 10 years and the road to the beach ends quite literally at the top of the cliff (TG 381311). A couple of miles north, Walcott is protected by hard defences and a long series of groynes which presumably deprives Happisburgh of material that might form a first line of defence from the waves.

A couple of miles south of Happisburgh, a relatively recent technique has been used. A reinforced concrete sea wall was constructed at Sea Palling in stages from 1953 to 1989, when fishtail groynes were proposed. These, however, would have obstructed the littoral drift and deprived the beaches further on of its benefit. In 1991, offshore reefs were proposed, of stone and concrete units sufficiently large and strong to resist the action of the sea and still the onshore waves. Initially modelled by computer, they were built in two phases, in 1994 and 1997 respectively, while their effects were observed, and the original third phase was found to be unnecessary. Although not the earliest – a scheme off the north Wirral coast was built in 1981 – they are still an unusual feature of the coastline.

87 (Right) Failed sea defences, Happisburgh. Houses to the right have been washed away.

88 Sea defences, Walcott.

89 Sea defences, Sea Palling.

Even more serious in terms of life and private property have been the great storm surges. In 1662 Sir William Dugdale, in *The History of Imbanking and Draining of divers Fens and Marshes*, listed many sea defences going back to earliest recorded times, and commissioners to maintain them were appointed under an Act of 1549. Nevertheless, the materials and technology available could not always cope. At Horsey Gap on the Norfolk coast (TM 478227) the sea broke through in December 1287 and several more times; as late as 1938, 7,469 acres there were flooded. The weak spot was the former outflow of the Hundred River; William Smith, the geologist, was consulted after some breaches in 1805. After 1812 the river and all of the drainage of this area was turned around to flow into the River Thurne and so to the south.

The floods of 31 January 1953 were particularly devastating. More than 200 people were drowned and more than half of the East Anglian coastlands were flooded. Canvey Island was completely underwater. At that time more than 90 per cent of sea defences along the eastern coast consisted of earthen embankments. Although hard defences have been put in

90 *Holmes Showroom, Norwich.*

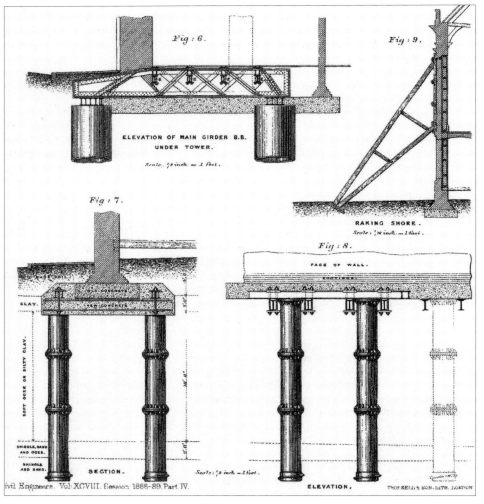

91 *Great Yarmouth Town Hall underpinning (Minutes of Proceedings of the Institution of Civil Engineers).*

place since then, where there is substantial industrial or residential property at risk, such as Canvey Island, they are not always cost-effective and may also have adverse environmental effects. A number of methods have been used to give or assist natural protection. Beach replenishment, restoring a beach to its original profile using sand from licensed offshore areas, pumping it ashore and spreading it, has been used to good effect but cannot be regarded as permanent. Between Hunstanton and Heacham hard defences were constructed after the 1953 floods, when 65 people died in the area. Littoral drift continued and sand and shingle from the area accumulated at Snettisham Scalp. In 1990/1 some of this was recycled and 400,000 cubic metres of sand dredged from the mouth of the River Humber was spread ashore. Further replenishment has been required since then.

Most recently, 'managed retreat' has become a favoured option in appropriate areas, for economic and environmental reasons. At Wallasea Island, opposite Burnham-on-Crouch, an area reclaimed in late medieval times, a breach in the sea wall has been deliberately made to allow the beach to act as the defence.

EARTHWORKS

It has been noted earlier that the Sea Bank and the Cambridgeshire lodes may have been built in Anglo-Saxon times. Another major civil engineering work that is generally ascribed to that period is the series of great earthworks that run roughly parallel to each other in south-east Cambridgeshire – **Devil's Ditch (C27)**, Fleam Dyke, High Ditch, Brent Ditch and Bran or Heydon Ditch.

STRUCTURES

Buildings, at least until the advent of skyscrapers, do not generally fall within the scope of civil engineering, but there are a few examples in East Anglia of earlier buildings that required expertise in structural engineering. One of the most remarkable is the octagon above the crossing of **Ely Cathedral (C14)**. Massive timber sections, each weighing about ten tons, had to be raised around 100ft above the cathedral floor and held in place until they could act together as a unit.

An idea of the machinery that might have been used during this operation can be gained from inspecting the medieval crane that still exists inside the north-western tower of **Peterborough Cathedral (C23)**. It was operated by men 'climbing' on rungs protruding each side of a central timber wheel. Later examples were often designed for animal power inside a cage formed by two wheels, boarded together at their rims, such as those at Harwich (**E9**) and Berden in Essex. It is interesting that the prison treadwheel was invented by an engineer from East Anglia, Sir William Cubitt.

Much later and much smaller than Ely Cathedral is St Nicholas' Church in Harwich. It was built in 1820-2 and is interesting for its early use of cast iron for structural members. The better-known St George's Church in Liverpool was designed in 1813, but the nave columns at St Nicholas dispense with some of the lateral bracing in the earlier church. Another interesting building is the shop now known as the Crystal Palace, in Cattle Market, Norwich. It was built in 1863 with a cast-iron and glass façade for Holmes, the engineers. The earliest example in Britain is Gardner's Warehouse in Jamaica Street, Glasgow, which dates from 1855-6. The other well-known examples in Liverpool were built in 1864 and 1866, so this one in Norwich is among the earliest of its type.

Civil engineers are also involved in the conservation of buildings, particularly but not exclusively where foundations are involved. Two notable examples in East Anglia are the restoration of the west tower of **Ely Cathedral (C15)** and the underpinning of **Great Yarmouth Town Hall (N8)**.

92 *Revolving tower, Great Yarmouth (demolished).*

One curiosity, alas now demolished, was a revolving observation tower. It was an American invention and a London engineer, Thomas Warwick, married the sister of one of the patentees. He decided to build the first in this country at Great Yarmouth, on a site next to the Britannia Pier. The Corporation leased the land to him in March 1897 on condition that the tower must not be less than 120ft high. Perhaps mindful of the problems with the town hall, it was built on a bed of concrete eight feet thick, but it was erected with remarkable speed and opened on 19 June 1897. A car revolved round the columns of the tower as it rose and descended on a system of ropes and weights powered by a steam engine; electricity to rotate and light the car was generated on the premises. The tower had a chequered history, both structurally and financially, and was eventually demolished in 1941 to provide steel for the war effort. Others were built at Southend, Scarborough, Douglas and Cleethorpes; the first three had short lives but the structure at Cleethorpes was relocated for use as a water tower and survived until 1959.

Another short-lived enterprise was the Reno Electric Stairway at Clacton. It was built in 1902 to a design by an American, Jesse Reno, who had built a successful prototype at Coney Island six years earlier. Trying to promote uses for his invention, he built an escalator with a 40ft rise up the cliffs at Clacton, but the novelty wore off and it lasted only until 1908. Further development led to its extensive adoption on London Underground, where it enjoyed a long life.

The structures that do remain, and the other works highlighted in these chapters, are described in the following county gazetteers.

This section of the book is a descriptive list of civil engineering works, not only many of those referred to in previous chapters but many other sites which further illustrate the contribution of the civil engineer to mankind's progress over the last four centuries.

The sites are arranged by county and location, and a county map shows the approximate position of each site. For each site the following information is given:

- The location (name of town or village) with street name etc. where necessary;
- The national grid reference;
- A brief description of the work;
- If necessary the accessibility of the site and any access charges if appropriate.

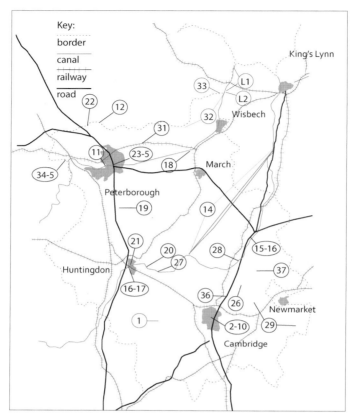

Map of Cambridgeshire.

C1. Bourn Windmill
C2. Cheddars Lane Sewage Pumping Station
C3. Clare College Bridge
C4. Garret Hostel Bridge
C5. Great, or Magdalene Bridge
C6. Mathematical Bridge
C7. St John's College Bridges
C8. Trinity College Bridge
C9. Hobson's Conduit
C10. Trinity College Conduit
C11. Ferry Bridge
C12. Deeping Gate Bridge
C13. Old and New Bedford Rivers
C14. Ely Cathedral Octagon
C15. Ely Cathedral West Tower's stabilisation
C16. Ely causeways
C17. Chinese Bridge
C18. Morton's Leam
C19. Holme Fen posts
C20. Houghton Mill
C21. Huntingdon Bridge
C22. Lolham Bridges
C23. Peterborough Cathedral medieval crane
C24. Nene Railway Bridge
C25. Tracked Hovercraft
C26. Reach Lode
C27. St Ives Bridge
C28. Stretham Pumping Station
C29. Devil's Ditch
C30. Swaffham & Bottisham Fen
C31. Thorney Tankyard
C32. North Level Main Drain
C33. Tydd Protection Sluice
C34. New Bridge
C35. Old Bridge
C36. Car Dyke
C37. Wicken Fen Windpump

BOURN

93 *Bourn Windmill.*

C1. Bourn Windmill (TL 312580) is a post mill claimed to be the oldest remaining windmill in Britain, although the mill at Pitstone in Buckinghamshire is the earliest dated mill. Built almost entirely of wood, there has inevitably been a continual process of repair and renewals over the years. At Bourn a deed of 1653 refers to the mill having changed hands in 1636. Repairs or rebuilding is shown by dates 1742, 1758 and 1874 carved in the mill.

The buck, or body, of the mill is the smallest in the country – 10ft 3in by 14ft 6in and overall height 31ft 6in – despite having been extended to the rear at some time. Also unusual is the fact that it is carried by upper and lower side girts attached to two vertical members at each end of the crowntree instead of horizontal side girts. Two of the four cloth sails have been replaced by shuttered sails.

The mill continued to work until 1927 when its sails were broken by a gale. It was taken over for preservation in 1931. Further extensive repairs were carried out in 1965, when steel angles were introduced to strengthen the buck, without spoiling its appearance, and in 1976 following storm damage. The mill is owned by the Cambridge Preservation Society, who open it to the public about once a month. Their website is www.cpswandlebury.org. There is a small car park just west of the mill, but no signpost to it on the road. (HEW 0690)

CAMBRIDGE

94 *Cheddars Lane Pumping Station, Cambridge.*

C2. Cheddars Lane Sewage Pumping Station (TL 465593) was the first example in the country of a combined waste disposal plant. It was built in 1894 for the Cambridge University & Town Water Company. Traditionally, the sewers of Cambridge discharged directly into the River Cam. The Rivers Pollution Act of 1876 made it possible for individuals to sue the responsible sanitary authority, who in Cambridge at that time were the town's improvement commissioners. The commissioners consulted Sir Joseph Bazalgette, the Engineer to the Metropolitan Board of Works, but his scheme was considered too expensive and was shelved. A subsequent scheme commissioned from Henry Law and George Chatterton – consulting engineers who had worked with Bazalgette and the Metropolitan Board – was also dropped. In 1888 the existing sewers were found to be in a very poor state, and the need for a comprehensive scheme of reconstruction was recognised at last. Two schemes were put forward, one by a councillor for a system constructed entirely by tunnelling, and the other by John T. Wood, the borough surveyor, involving only limited tunnelling. James Mansergh was asked to compare and report on the two schemes, and came out decidedly in favour of Wood's, with some proposed amendments. Even so, work did not commence until late 1894.

The buildings of the pumping station were erected by Kerridge & Shaw, contractors, for £3,192 14s. od. The chimney, which cost £1,554, is 175ft high. It sits on a plinth of moulded stone and is square at the base, octagonal above. The chimney proper has four sections, each 35ft 6in high, the lowest three bricks thick, reducing by half a brick each time to one and a half bricks at the top.

The sewage was delivered to a well under the engine house, from which it was pumped through a 24in cast-iron rising main to a 70-acre sewage farm at Milton, 3,593 yards away. The cast-iron pipe was supplied by S.W. Pattinson of Ruskington, Lincoln for £5,961 7s. 6d. The invert level at the pumping station is 27½ft below Jesus Weir, and the outlet 22½ft above, so the rise is 50ft.

The pumps were supplied under a contract with Hathorn, Davey & Co. for £5,450. Two horizontal compound condensing rotative engines, with 22in and 44in cylinders with 4ft stroke, were designed to work together or separately. Two single-acting lift-and-force pumps, each 34in diameter and with four-foot stroke, were attached to each engine. At 80psi, 250,000 gallons of sewage pumped per hour. Initially the sewage was spread untreated on the land at Milton, owing to a dispute about the best method of treating it.

The engines' boilers were of the Mills and Babcock type. Part of the heat for them was provided by a refuse destructor, an early though not the earliest example. Dust carts from the town came in along a bank constructed off Cheddars Lane and emptied their loads into bottom-opening iron trucks on rails. These were drawn mechanically above the furnaces, into which they emptied their loads. The destructor was operating by November 1895, when a man from Liverpool with experience of the destructor there was employed to give advice on the best method of working it.

The works were modified subsequently, in 1909 by the installation of gas engines coupled to Gwynne's pumps, in 1923 by a coke-fired boiler, and in 1937 by the addition of a 114hp electric motor. The plant continued to operate until 1968. It has now been adapted to form the Cambridge Museum of Technology. It is open on Sunday afternoons, monthly in winter and weekly in summer. (HEW 2709)

Bridges along the Backs

Going downriver from the Mill, the head of the navigation, you encounter Silver Street Bridge, 1959 by Sir Edwin Lutyens on the site of Cambridge's original second bridge, Small Bridges; **Mathematical Bridge (C6)**; King's College Bridge, 1819 by William Wilkins; **Clare College Bridge (C3)**; **Garret Hostel Bridge (C4)**; **Trinity College Bridge (C8)**; St John's College Old Bridge, 1712, often attributed to Sir Christopher Wren or Nicholas Hawksmoor but in fact by Robert Grumbold; **St John's College New Bridge (C7)**, the Bridge of Sighs; and **Magdalene Bridge (C5)**, on the site of the original Great Bridge. Garret Hostel is the only one that carries a public right of way; the others may be seen when the colleges are open to the public, usually on payment of an admission charge.

C3. Clare College Bridge (TL 446584) is the oldest remaining bridge in Cambridge, having been erected in 1639-40. The college had begun to replace its original 14th-century buildings, and wanted access to the west side of the river in order to bring in materials. Thomas Grumbold, a stonemason from the Weldon area of limestone quarries in Northamptonshire who was working at the college, supplied a drawing of a bridge, for which he was paid three shillings on 18 January 1639. Although he could simply have been the draughtsman, it is probable that the design was his. The contractor's name is known – payments totalling £284 13s. 8d. to Richard Chamberlayne have been identified in the college accounts.

The bridge is one of the earliest in England of classical design. It is built of ashlar limestone from Ketton, near Stamford, with some Barnack stone reused from a previous

structure. Its three arches each span slightly more or less than 21ft and its width of 14ft between the ornamental balustrades was generous for its time. With the passage of time the bridge, and particularly its western arch, had deformed and a survey in 1972 suggested that it was no longer sufficiently strong for its purpose, so repairs were carried out to safeguard it for the future. (HEW 0227)

C4. Garret Hostel Bridge (TL 446585) is a prestressed concrete footbridge with a very shallow structural depth. It has been for foot traffic only ever since it was first constructed in the 15th century, the third of the bridges over the Cam. Of timber, it was replaced by James Essex in 1769, based on the design he had contracted to build 20 years earlier for Queens' College **(C6)**. A bridge of 1814 was short-lived and was superseded in cast iron to the design of William Chadwell Mylne in 1837. When differential settlement caused this to fracture, an elegant portal frame structure in prestressed concrete was built in 1960. It gives better clearance for those in punts below, but is a much steeper pull for cyclists. (HEW 0659)

C5. Great, or Magdalene Bridge (TL 447589) is, for its date of 1823, a rather archaic design, harking back to Coslany Bridge at Norwich **(N18)**. It was said to have been designed by Arthur Browne, an architect of Norwich, whose name is cast on the bridge, though there was also input from Benjamin Bevan, an engineer from Leighton Buzzard. It cost £2,350. When it showed signs of settlement in the 1970s it was proposed to rebuild it entirely, but the resulting outcry caused a change of mind and in 1982 steel girders were placed inside the cast iron to take the load, leaving the façade as it was before. (HEW 1340)

95 *Garret Hostel Bridge, Cambridge (1960).*

C6. Queens' College, or Mathematical, Bridge (TL 446581) is a rare example of a type of timber bridge that enjoyed a brief popularity in the middle of the 18th century. It is

96 *Magdalene (or Great) Bridge, Cambridge.*

a successor of two bridges from the 16th century giving access from Queens' College to fields on the west side of the river. The other bridge no longer exists and this one was rebuilt in 1700 and again in 1750. This last design was provided by William Etheridge, who had been the fore-man carpenter at Westminster Bridge and is based on the formwork he had built for the stone arches there. Originally built between July 1749 and September 1750, decay in the timber has required it to be rebuilt to the original design twice; the last occasion was in 1904. Although it looks like an arch, the timbers are all straight lengths, bolted together to form a truss.

The contractor for this bridge, James Essex, built a similar bridge in Garret Hostel Lane (**C4**) that he called a mathematical bridge. That one has been replaced and the name has stuck to this one. (HEW 0469)

C7. St John's College Bridges (TL 446588) are two ornamental bridges from different periods, serving two different purposes. The Old Bridge, like other college bridges across the Backs, gave access to the fields on the west side of the river. Sir Christopher Wren was consulted and some preliminary work was done in 1696-8, but it was designed and built in 1709-12 by Robert Grumbold, from a well-known family of masons and quarrymen from Northamptonshire. It has semi-circular arches and a central span of 20ft, with a baroque elevation typical of architectural practice at the time.

97 *Queens' College (or Mathematical) Bridge.*

The New Bridge was built in 1831 to a design by Henry Hutchinson, whose brief was to provide access to the college's new buildings across the river without allowing public access. The result was an enclosed structure on an elliptical arch of 40ft span, called the Bridge of Sighs because of a faint resemblance to the structure in Venice. (HEW 1941)

C8. Trinity College Bridge (TL 446586) was designed by James Essex, the carpenter who had earlier built the **Mathematical Bridge (C6)**, but this is a restrained masonry design. It was built in 1763-5 with the newly fashionable elliptical arches, and the limestone ashlar was sourced from Ketton near Stamford and Portland in Dorset. The result is a slight but noticeable difference

98 *St Johns College New Bridge, Cambridge.*

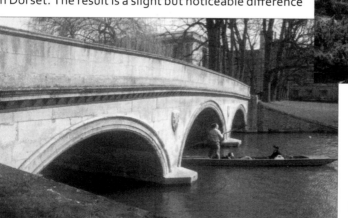

99 *Trinity College Bridge, Cambridge.*

in colour that defines the different elements of the structure, a feature that had been used by Robert Adam in his bridge upriver at Audley End in 1762-3. (HEW 0841)

C9. Hobson's Conduit, Cambridge (TL 462542 to TL 450585) was an early water supply that did not owe its origin to a religious foundation. It was an aqueduct leading water from Nine Wells, in the parish of Great Shelford south of Cambridge, into the city. An open watercourse from its source as far as a point by the junction of Trumpington Road and Lensfield Road, it was conducted thence in three branches, in places through underground lead pipes or else in open runnels along the streets.

The original impetus was provided by the need to do something about the unsanitary condition of the King's Ditch. This had been constructed at the command of King Henry III about the year 1265 as a defence for the town, but over the following three centuries had degenerated to an obnoxious sewer. An Act for the New River from Hertfordshire into London had been passed in 1571, though not put into execution. In 1574, Dr Perne, the master of Peterhouse, who would have known of that Act, suggested turning Vicar's Brook into the King's Ditch in order to flush it out. Nothing was done at the time but the scheme was revived and carried out in 1610.

100 *Hobson's Conduit, Cambridge.*

The names of those who planned and surveyed the project are not known with certainty. It is often attributed to Edward Wright of Caius College, a mathematician who put the art of navigation on a scientific basis, but it may well have been based on a survey by Richard Browne, the Keeper of the Water Mills at Lynn, at the time of the abortive scheme in 1574. The source chosen was not the nearest possible, for there was one at Cherry Hinton. However, that led naturally to an outfall below the town and would have required more artificial cutting to bring it into the King's Ditch. By utilising the course of Vicar's Brook for two miles, only a short length at the start and the last half-mile to Lensfield Road would need to be constructed if Nine Wells was used. One consequence though is that the fall is very uneven – 7ft 9in in the first two miles and virtually none in the last half mile. The channel itself was built to be 15ft wide at the top and four feet deep. Part of it, running alongside the University's Botanic Gardens, is raised on an embankment. It was constructed at the joint expense of the town and university. There is no evidence that Thomas Hobson (1544-1630), the well-known carrier who gave rise to the phrase 'Hobson's choice', had anything to do with its funding, though he was one of several benefactors who subsequently provided for its maintenance. It was partly successful, cleaning out the western half of the ditch but not the eastern, which lay beyond the slight ridge that carried the original road to the bridge over the River Cam.

London's New River had been constructed in 1609-13 to supply the city with potable water. There was constant communication between London and the University of Cambridge, with travellers often going via Ware, so it is not surprising that in 1614 it was decided to extend the Cambridge leat to Mill Lane and add a branch to a fountain – also called a conduit – in Market Hill, to supply the townspeople. A third line to Emmanuel and Christ's Colleges was added in 1631.

The channel of the first line along Trumpington Street was originally in the street itself, about one third of the way across. Soon after 1794, runnels were provided instead at each kerb; these still exist. Parts of all three lines within the city were laid underground in lead pipes, which lasted until 1842 when they were replaced by glazed pipes. By 1856 the growing need for water had rendered Hobson's Conduit inadequate and a pumped supply from the River Cam superseded it. The conduit in Market Hill was removed to Lensfield Road though a new and less ornate conduit with a pumped supply was built later in Market Hill. The visible remains include:

(a)   an obelisk at Nine Wells erected in 1861, after the Conduit had been superseded. It bears inscriptions commemorating several benefactors. It lies inside a small copse and can be reached by a public footpath leading from Graham's Road at TL 471543;

(b)   the embankment running between Trumpington Road and the Botanic Gardens;

(c)   the Conduit, resited at the corner of Trumpington Road and Lensfield Road;

(d)   the runnels in Trumpington Street.

Also of interest are four cast-iron bridges over the channel, leading to the Botanic Gardens and Brookside. Cast by the local company of Hurrell, they bear the dates 1850 and 1851. They are listed Grade II. (HEW 1942)

C10. Trinity College Conduit, Cambridge (TL 429596 to TL 447586) was a very early piped water supply. The first conduit to the town was almost certainly an open-air stone channel, which was mentioned in the rent roll of Barnwell Priory in 1295. It was on a different line from the existing conduit, and was sold to the town c.1424.

The Franciscan (Grey) Friars bought land for a new conduit on 5 November 1325 to bring water to their monastery site, now occupied by Sidney Sussex College. The spring was in a field called Bradrusshe, off what is now Conduit Head Road. There the ground consists of gravel overlying a layer of gault, which provides an impermeable

101   *Trinity College Conduit Head, Cambridge.*

layer to retain the groundwater in the gravel. The springs are channelled along a brick drain to a filter, from which a short length of lead pipe leads south to the Conduit House. This is a rectangular building 9½ft by 9½ft, built of oolite stone, possibly built in 1327. Inside is a lead tank five feet long, two feet wide and three feet deep. The Conduit House is now in the grounds of a private house.

Work started on 1 May 1327. The conduit was 1,467 ells, or about 5,500ft long; the pipe was originally of seamed lead. On the dissolution of monasteries, ownership of the conduit passed to Trinity College. The conduit fed taps in the college dining hall and stables, as well as the octagonal fountain in the Great Court erected in 1601-2 and largely rebuilt in 1736. The springs provided about 13,000 gallons of water per day, and still provide part of the supply to the fountain, though the water to the tap near the main gate is not potable. A tablet in the Conduit House records 'From this reservoir the whole line was relaid with new lead pipe during the years 1841 and 1849', a two-inch diameter seamless lead pipe replacing the original seamed one.

Small marker stones along its length exist(ed) at the crossings of Madingley Road, Hedgerley Close, Bulstrode Gardens, Wilberforce Road, Grange Road, St John's College Playing Fields, Queens' Road and St John's College Grove. The conduit can be seen in the bed of Bin Brook. (HEW 2708)

CASTOR

C11. Ferry Bridge (TL 143984) is an elegant ashlar bridge. It was, according to a tablet on its east face, 'built at the sole cost and charge of Rt. Hon. William, Earl Fitzwilliam'. He had been the 3rd Baron Fitzwilliam and was raised to the rank of earl in 1716, the year that the bridge was built. The Fitzwilliam family lived at Milton Hall, a large estate immediately north of Gunwade Ferry over the River Nene, which this bridge replaced. It provided the only crossing of the river between Peterborough three miles to the east and Wansford (**C35**) five miles to the west. It was a private bridge and when Daniel Defoe went to cross it in 1724 he was charged 2s. 6d., of which he would 'only say this, that I think 'tis the only half crown toll in Britain'.

It has three semi-circular arches which spring well above normal water level, though the river can rise dramatically. Triangular cutwaters and fluted keystones provide relief to the fine ashlar limestone. The north abutment contains two small rooms, with doors on the east side and small bull's-eye windows on the west.

When Castor was bypassed in 1991, Ferry Lodge stood in the path of the upgraded road. It was removed stone by stone and rebuilt further to the north-west on the Milton estate. Ferry Bridge now gives access to the recreational areas of Peterborough's Nene Park. There is a car park at the north end of the bridge. (HEW 1763)

DEEPING GATE

C12. Deeping Gate Bridge (TF 150094) is one of the few sizeable bridges constructed in England in the mid-17th century. It carries the date '1651' on its south-western cutwater, a time when the Civil War was just ending and political uncertainty still prevailed. The River Welland was navigable here, but the three arch spans are conservative, being only

103 *Deeping Gate Bridge.*

18ft, 19ft and 18ft 6in. The vault of the central arch has been rebuilt at some time in engineering brick. The quality of the limestone masonry is good, with double arch rings in two orders, each with a small chamfer, and a deep label above. The roadway is only 13ft wide, so the substantial triangular cutwaters are carried up to provide refuges at road level. An ashlar band at road level carries parapets of smaller and darker walling stone. Though not adventurous structurally, the bridge is attractive. (HEW 0063)

EARITH

C13. Old and New Bedford Rivers are the most prominent features of the two major campaigns of drainage carried out for the 4th and 5th Earls of Bedford and their co-Adventurers in the 17th century. The old course of the River Great Ouse flowed in a great loop from the foot of the isle of Ely at Earith past Ely, Littleport and Outwell, and, joined by the Nene, entered the Wash through Wisbech. In the 13th century its course became blocked and its outlet

104 *Bedford Level Washes (this photograph was taken from the same position as Fig. 79, but looking in the opposite direction) (Cambridge University Collection of Air Photos).*

diverted northwards from Denver to King's Lynn, whose inhabitants then obtained a charter from the king allowing them to stabilise the new channel. The river overflowed its banks regularly, flooding many thousands of acres of fen land adjoining. Any attempts to alleviate the problem were hampered until late Elizabethan times by lack of the necessary large sums of capital. In 1589 the Privy Council required Ralph Agas of Stoke-by-Nayland, John Hexham of Huntingdon and Humphry Bradley of Bergen-op-Zoom to survey the country and prepare plans for a comprehensive scheme of drainage. Bradley presented his report on 3 December. His main contribution was to show that drainage by gravity was possible, provided the circuitous course of the rivers could be shortened (as had been done a century earlier by Bishop Morton on the River Nene – **C18**). A further report by Bradley on 3 April 1593 proposed a central authority to deal with the various ownerships and tenures of the land and, probably as a first step only, a new cut from Welney to the River Ouse. No action ensued. The next major report was made by John Hunt, helped by the map of the whole fens made by William Hayward in 1604. With the backing of Sir John Popham, the Lord Chief Justice, Hunt and the Commissioners of Sewers (the local land drainage authority) undertook a tour of the area in June 1605 at which, among other things, Hunt proposed a cut-off channel from Earith in a straight line to some suitable place near Salters Lode (where the Well Creek joins the River Ouse). The Commission then met at Wisbech on 13 July 1605 and passed a 'law and ordinance' allowing and obliging Popham and others to drain the lands between the course of the Ouse (now the Old West River) and the River Welland, an area of about 230,000 acres. Almost immediately work began on the drain now known as Popham's Eau, from Nordelph to the Old Nene, which had been completed when Popham and his colleagues sought an Act of Parliament in February 1606 to confirm the legality of their proceedings. The bill was rejected in May 1606 and again in 1607. The banks of the Eau broke during a great storm in March 1606 and although some repairs and additional banking were done over the next four years, Popham's death in June 1607 effectively put an end to the first great scheme for a general drainage of the Fens.

In 1621, after two years of unsuccessful attempts to revive interest in a general scheme for the Fens, King James I declared himself willing to undertake the work. However, lack of capital was still a major obstacle and it was probable that the king sought advice from the Netherlands, from where finance might also be available. (Sir) Cornelius Vermuyden was consulted and no doubt made use of the earlier plans noted above, but still no progress was made. Interest in the Fens revived in 1629 when a team led by Sir Anthony Thomas made some proposals. These were rejected as Thomas was unwilling to reveal sufficient detail for the Commissioners of Sewers to make a proper assessment of his plans. The new king, Charles I, now ordered the commissioners to take a more active role and, led by the 4th Earl of Bedford, the largest landowner in the Fens, they consulted Vermuyden by July 1630. A statement of intent to contract with Vermuyden to drain all of the fens south of the River Glen, in Lincolnshire, about 360,000 acres, was issued on 1 September 1630, but, because of problems elsewhere, Vermuyden seems to have lost the confidence of his Netherlands backers and this, with local opposition, led Bedford to undertake the work himself, with Andrewes Burrell as engineer. One of the 11 works undertaken was the (Old) Bedford River, 21 miles long from Earith to Denver, to cut 9½ miles off the length of the Ouse, thereby increasing the gradient and improving the flow of flood water. It was 70ft wide, with banks seven feet high, not more than 200ft apart, and cost about £26,000. The widths of the cut and space between the banks were much less than Hunt had proposed, and the first flood that came down the river broke the banks. Also, silting at the outfall, which was tidal, soon occurred and the river, with the other 10 works undertaken, provided relief from flooding during the summer months only.

The Earl of Bedford's funds being effectively exhausted, in 1638 the king again took the lead, and received proposals from Burrell (October 1638) and Vermuyden (January 1639) for keeping the Fens dry in winter too. Vermuyden's were accepted and some work was carried out around the River Nene in 1640-1, until lack of funds forced a halt. Shortly afterwards, further work was prevented by the outbreak of the Civil War.

An 'Act for the draining the Great Level of the Fenns' was passed on 26 May 1649 and the fifth Earl of Bedford, who had succeeded his father, and his associates immediately formed the Company of Adventurers to carry out the remaining work. After much discussion on the nature of his role, Vermuyden was appointed Director of Works on 25 January 1650. The first year's work enabled the North and Middle Levels to be declared winter grounds and in March 1651 attention turned to the South Level. At this stage Vermuyden abandoned his idea of a cut-off channel to the east of the Level (revived and executed on a slightly larger scale in 1954-64) and instead concentrated on improving the River Ouse. He cut the New Bedford River or Hundred-Foot Drain, generally parallel to and half a mile east of the Old Bedford River, 100ft wide, with banks 10ft high tapering from 50ft wide at the base to 10ft at the top, with earth brought from Over (four miles south of Earith) rather than the peaty fenland soil. The line was not precisely straight as it had to detour 'inland' slightly to avoid high ground at Sutton. The land between the outer banks of both Bedford Rivers became a receptacle to hold flood waters until they could be safely discharged. This work, with a double-arch sasse (or navigable sluice) across the mouth of the River Ouse at Denver, was declared by Vermuyden to be complete on 17 February 1653 and accepted as such by the company a month later. Work on ancillary items continued until 1656.

The improved drainage resulted in the peat level shrinking, so the water level in the river became higher than the surrounding land. The outfall goes through stable silt and so the banks of the rivers had to be raised, soon necessitating the use of wind power pumps to raise water from the dykes. Because the banks are in places confined between

the river and external infrastructure they have become narrower for their height than would be desirable and require regular maintenance.

Today in normal water conditions, the Hundred-Foot is tidal, taking water from below Brownshill Staunch (TL 369727). Winter floodwater is taken off through the Earith Sluice, rebuilt in 1950 and replacing the earlier Nine-hole and Seven-hole Sluices, and it is directed via the Old Bedford River onto the Washes, which provide a winter wetland habitat and summer grazing. The Hermitage Sluice at Earith regulates the flow in to the Ely Ouse, with a 15ft-wide lock for navigation.

The two Bedford Rivers collect the local drainage from the South Level on the right-hand side and the Middle Level on the left-hand side. The Counter Drain collects water outside the line of the Old Bedford River. At Welches Dam an old modification to the original scheme directs the Counter Drain into the old course of the Old Bedford, while the Old Bedford bends into the Washes, entering a third channel known as the River Delph. This channel flows through the Washes for 10 miles before crossing over to discharge through Welmore Lake Sluice into the tidal Hundred-Foot Drain. The remains of an early pointing door sluice are visible on the north bank. Before this, the Washes were drained by breaching an earth dam each spring.

A contemporary Vermuyden drain, the Forty-Foot, joins the course of the Old Bedford at Welches Dam. Originally designed to discharge into the Old Bedford, the Forty Foot water level is now some six to eight feet too low. There is a navigation lock which is deteriorating rapidly. Approaching Denver the land of the South Level is eight feet below normal high water and up to 16ft below exceptional high tides.

The Hundred-Foot flows freely into the River Great Ouse at Denver some 11 miles above Kings Lynn. There is a complex of modern sluices, including the 1832 Rennie sluice controlling the flow of the Ely Ouse, and the inlet to the 1964 Relief Channel. The Old Bedford now carrying the water from the Counter Drain, is sluiced into the River Great Ouse through a modern steel-gated lock half a mile further downstream.

There are three modern crossings of the Washes, at Sutton Gault, Mepal and Welney. Mepal road crossing is the only one that is dry all the year round. At Welney, the crossing of the Hundred-Foot is a modern bridge, replacing the former chain suspension bridge by Captain Sir Samuel Brown.

ELY

C14. Ely Cathedral Octagon (TL 541802) is an outstanding example of early structural engineering. As originally built in the 12th century, Ely Cathedral had a conventional square tower above the main crossing of the nave and transepts. This tower collapsed in 1322 and out of this catastrophe arose the supreme architectural glory of Ely and one of the greatest feats of structural engineering in the Middle Ages. The reconstruction is associated with the name of Alan de Walsingham, the cathedral's Sacrist, and he was certainly in overall charge of the work. It was probably he who decided to remove the four piers supporting the towers and to encase the eight piers adjacent, on strengthened foundations, in order to support an octagonal lantern. The piers were capped at about mid-height of the triforium, above which Gothic arches in turn support an octagonal masonry tower. This was complete by 1328. Within and above this was a massive timber lantern, whose design was the responsibility of William Hurley, the King's Carpenter.

105a and b
Ely Cathedral octagon.

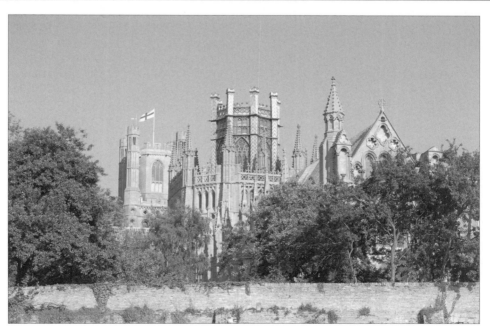

The octagon contains the lower part of the timber frame that supports the lantern. Eight corner posts were erected first in vertical slots in the masonry. These were then tied back against the masonry and strained apart by horizontal members, and a triangular radial structure was introduced at each of the eight to support the lower sill at the top level of the verticals. The eight apices of the lower sill each supported one of the vertical great posts of the lantern, which was framed internally by an upper sill at about three-quarters of its height. Each post is 63ft long, 20 by 32in in section. External diagonal stays from about one third of the way up the great posts led down to the feet of the corner posts. The timbers were raised almost 100ft above the floor and held in position on falsework until the structure was complete.

In 1757 James Essex, a carpenter/architect of Cambridge (who built the Mathematical and Trinity College Bridges there (**C6** and **C8**)) prepared a report on the structure. Finding considerable evidence of decay, he made repairs but also extensive changes. The main stays supporting the lower sill, being curved, mimicked the form of the stone vaulting and so were aesthetically satisfactory, but would have been overstressed by the weight of the lantern. Essex added extra stays to deal with this problem but removed the wall posts and the external flying buttresses. He also altered the external appearance of the structure by adding stone spirelets to the outer corners of the octagon and pinnacles to the octagon's great posts.

Essex's repairs seem to have dealt with the structural problems in the octagon, but in 1862-3 George Gilbert Scott made a report, on the basis of which he undertook work to restore the octagon to much of its original visual state. This work included removing the pinnacles (but not the spirelets) and restoring the flying buttresses, though with additional masonry in the long sides of the supporting octagon for the buttresses to bear against. (HEW 0757)

C15. Ely Cathedral West Tower's stabilisation is a good example of modern structural philosophy applied to conservation of a major medieval building. The walls of the west tower of Ely Cathedral are about three metres thick and solid up to +23m; from there up to +46m (constructed probably by 1189) they consist of two leaves of limestone, about 1,500mm and 800mm thick with a passageway 800mm wide between. The outer, 1,500mm, leaf has two 'skins' of limestone each about 150mm thick with poor-quality rubble hearting between. About 1380/1400 the tower was extended upwards, to +59m, but whereas the Norman work is square in plan, the newer work is octagonal, with separate stair towers carried up from each corner of the lower tower. The masonry in the later stages is solid, about 500mm thick. The tower had settled, probably over a period of time after each of the building phases, and cracks had appeared in the stonework. In the 1750s, as part of his restoration of the cathedral, James Essex had made repairs, but by 1845, when George Gilbert Scott, the architect, was in charge of the fabric, significant further work was necessary.

In 1860 Scott inserted the first of a number of wrought-iron ties diagonally across the tower and through the masonry to be anchored outside. Further ties were subsequently installed, both to contain the tower as a whole and to contain local bulging in the masonry.

By 1972 the masonry in the parapets and turrets was dangerous and the wrought-iron ties outside were rusting and causing serious damage. It was decided that it would be both prudent and economical to strengthen the tower at the same time as undertaking the urgent remedial work. The structural analysis undertaken by Professor Heyman, as consulting engineer to the Dean and Chapter, was based on the assumption that a masonry structure is an assemblage of dry stones, acting under gravity and in the

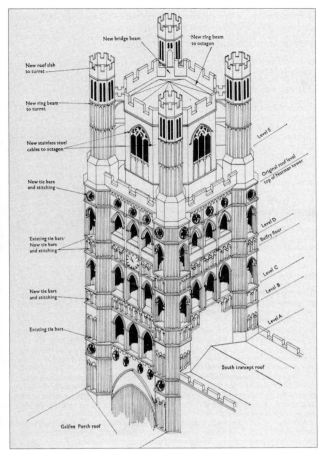

worst case by friction alone between the stones. It was necessary to be satisfied that there were no slender parts of the structure that might be liable to buckle. If this was so, it was sufficient to ensure that each part could bear a uniformly distributed stress to bear the weight from above; any excess strength in some parts of the structure would give an added margin of safety. For the west tower at Ely, this meant for example that the weak fill between the skins of the wall would be strengthened sufficiently to bear that notional stress.

The work that was undertaken in 1973-4 included introducing four ring beams into the lower two-thirds of the tower by 'stitching' with stainless-steel bars and grouting; three sets of stainless steel ties passing from face to face of the tower, one of which replaces some of Scott's work; inserting a reinforced concrete ring beam at the top of the belfry; and fixing and prestressing stainless-steel ties at a lower level in the belfry. Stainless-steel plates embedded behind the masonry surface act as anchorages and the general region was stitched so that the tie bar load is distributed. All of the external wrought-iron straps were removed, but internally they were generally in good condition and were only taken away where they obstructed the building. (HEW 0900)

106 *Ely Cathedral west tower, remedials (Proceedings of the Institution of Civil Engineers).*

107 *Haddenham Causeway.*

C16. Ely causeways are early-medieval engineered roads. Until the 12th century the island on which stands the town of Ely was accessible for much of the year only by boat. The nearest 'high' ground to this island was at Aldreth to the south, Stuntney to the east, Earith to the west and Littleport to the north. Although William the Conqueror had created a bridge to the island in order to suppress the revolt of Hereward the Wake, it is probable that this was a temporary expedient. However, the conversion of the abbey of Ely to a cathedral, with a shrine attracting pilgrims, called for some better, more permanent access.

Aldreth Causeway

There was a crossing of the Ouse at Aldreth from early times. In 1172-3 the considerable sum of £6 10s. 9d. was spent on a 'brethasch' or causeway, which suggests that at this time the original ferry to the mainland was being replaced by something more permanent. In the Middle Ages the causeway was the main Cambridge-Ely road. In 1279 a bridge is mentioned in addition to the causeway. Both had been out of repair for 16 years, but had lately been restored by the

bishop, who was responsible for their maintenance. His bailiff let the tolls for 20s. a year; horsemen paid ½d. each and foot passengers ¼d. Though an indulgence was granted for the repair of the causeway by Bishop Fordham in 1406, the duty of regular maintenance was in principle distributed among the customary tenants of the various episcopal manors. Even Outwell and Upwell, 20 miles away on the opposite side of the Liberty, were originally required to look after 44 perches of the causeway. About 1613 the bridge collapsed and was replaced by a ferry. This ferry was dangerous; by 1638 six or seven lives had been lost there. By 1662 the bridge had perhaps been rebuilt; it was certainly in existence again early in the 18th century, but in bad repair. Another partial collapse occurred in 1765, when the two middle piers fell down 'within a few minutes after two gentlemen had luckily got over' the bridge. This disaster was probably caused by the succession of wet seasons and floods of the early 1760s.

As early as 1676 the existence of an alternative entry into the Isle through Stretham is mentioned. This is the present main approach to the Isle from the south. In 1773 the Cambridge and Ely Turnpike Trust caused a survey to be made of two routes from Cambridge to Witcham, one by Aldreth and the other by Stretham; the former was shorter by just under a mile. By the late 18th century the Stretham route was brought into good repair, and with the alternative route formed by the road from Cottenham to Wilburton via Twenty Pence Bridge, the main stream of traffic was diverted from Aldreth causeway. The causeway, however, was still used fairly frequently until c.1870, and the bridge was rebuilt in 1901-2.

Stuntney or Soham Causeway

According to the *Liber Eliensis*, written by a monk of Ely in the later 12th century, the only way north from Soham was by boat or by sledging over the ice. During the time of Hervey le Breton, first Bishop of Ely (1109-33), after an Exning man had a vision about the need for a road linking Bury St Edmunds to Ely, a monk of Ely Priory called John undertook to construct a causeway from Ely to Stuntney towards Soham. It was built on bundles of reeds, and small bridges crossed the water channels. The priory thus became responsible for the maintenance of the causeway, which they did well for over 200 years, though from the late 14th century there were complaints of neglect. This responsibility devolved onto the Dean and Chapter of the Cathedral as successors to the priory after the dissolution of the monasteries, and continued well into the 18th century. From 1763 the road was a branch of the Cambridge and Ely Turnpike.

Haddenham or Earith Causeway

The bridge and causeway over Haddenham Fen, then known as 'Earith Causey,' were looked after by hermits in the 14th and 15th centuries. Indulgences were granted in 1397 for Richard de Grymston, a poor hermit, and in 1401 for Henry Bourne,to repair Earith Causeway. There is a record also of the 'profession' of John Thomson, hermit of Earith Causeway. By the early 18th century, and probably from c.1650, there was an important bridge across the Ouse at Earith Sluice, reached by a road leading north from Willingham alongside the lode and the Old West River. Before the construction of the Cambridge-Ely turnpike in 1768 it was said that the only carriage road between the two towns lay through Willingham village.

The causeways today

Aldreth Causeway is formally designated as a byway open to all traffic. It is carried on a low embankment with deep drainage ditches alongside. It does not appear to have been metalled, and in wet weather quite deep ruts can be formed in it.

Stuntney Causeway is the present A142 leading to Newmarket and Bury St Edmunds. Road improvements including the construction of the Stuntney bypass have rather diminished the appearance of a causeway captured in plate 7 of H.C. Darby's book *The Mediaeval Fenland*, published in 1940.

From the foot of Haddenham Hill, the Earith Causeway takes the A1123 towards St Ives and Huntingdon. It adopts a rather sinuous course to Earith Bridge, possibly due to variations in the ground conditions at the time it was formed. It, like the others, is carried on a low embankment, with drainage ditches on each side. (HEW 2696)

GODMANCHESTER
C17. Chinese Bridge (TL 244705) is a rare surviving example of an ornamental timber footbridge. It has a 60-foot span, with an eight-foot rise, over one branch of the River Ouse, just west of the town centre of Godmanchester. It carries a public footpath from the town to extensive walks along the river. A stone plaque at the eastern approach states that it was built to the design of James Gallier in 1827 and rebuilt in 1869 and 1960. It is his only known bridge in the United Kingdom; in 1832 he emigrated to the United States of America. The main arch springs from large blocks of sandstone (unusual in this area); the eastern one is inscribed 'T Lartin S Bates Building Committee' and the western one 'Erected AD 1827'. The abutments are of the local gault brick and curve outwards in plan away from the bridge, ending in circular piers. The abutment face slopes back radially to provide a direct springing for the timber.

The superstructure of the bridge consists in elevation of two timber arches of different radii, one above the other and trussed together by timber saltires. The lower arch consists of six lengths of timber, each five inches wide by seven inches deep, butted together and restrained by metal straps across the joints. The upper arch has four lengths, 4½in wide by six inches deep, connected similarly. The spandrel saltires are formed with timber 4½in wide by three inches deep. There are two frames as described above, one at each face of the bridge and there is an upper arch only under the centreline of the bridge. The two frames are connected by cross-timbers supporting further timber saltires and sway is prevented by metal rods crossing to each half of the bridge from one frame to the other. There are also timber knee braces from the abutments, outside the main structure. The footway consists of transverse timber planks, laid directly on top of the upper arches. There are 14 panels to each parapet, which is 3ft 6in deep, in what has been called Chippendale-Chinese style. The verticals pass down outside the upper arch and are bolted to it; the middle five are bolted to the lower arch also, which here is in contact with the upper and in fact cuts slightly into it.

In 1960 the superstructure was replaced, using greenheart timber. Each frame was assembled lying flat on its side on the ground before being reared and lifted into position by crane. In doing so, the crown sagged so that the rise is now less than it had been. In 1993 the parapets were replaced. Enquiries at Huntingdon and Cambridge Record Offices, the County Surveyor's Department and Godmanchester town council (the previous owner) have failed to locate any records of the bridge. (HEW 1943)

GUYHIRN
C18. Morton's Leam was the first major attempt to improve the drainage of the fens by cutting an artificial, shorter, channel for a major river in order to improve its flow.

As originally built c.1480 under the supervision of John Morton, Bishop of Ely, it was 12 miles long, 40ft broad, and four feet deep. It was dug from Stanground near Peterborough to Guyhirn near Wisbech, and by means of it and associated dams the flood waters in the Nene were carried to Wisbech directly, rather than following the circuitous course of the South Nene via Whittlesey Mere and Benwick to its confluence with the old River Ouse at Upwell. Built at the end of the Middle Ages, the Leam set an example for the drainage works which were to follow a century later.

Due to a lack of maintenance following the Dissolution of the Monasteries the Leam slowly became blocked. Just before the 17th century water was flowing from Guyhirn by Elm and Outwell to the Ouse, instead of taking its course directly through Wisbech to the sea. Morton's Leam was widened to 50ft by Andrewes Burrell in 1631. In 1640-1 (Sir) Cornelius Vermuyden constructed a bank along the south side of the Leam except at Whittlesey and made a start on a bank along the north side. Lack of funds in those troubled times forced a halt to the work, but it was resumed late in 1650 and both banks were completed by February 1651. Together they created a washland of about 3,000 acres to receive and hold flood waters.

109 *Holme Fen posts.*

A proposal by Humphry Smith 'for the more effectual draining and preservation of the North Level by making a new channel in the wash near the north bank of Morton's Leam for strengthening and raising that bank, the charge whereof will amount to £6,600' was put to the Bedford Level Corporation in May 1728. The Earls of Bedford and Lincoln advanced the capital and the work was almost certainly finished in 1730. Now known as Smith's Leam, it forms the main channel of the River Nene today and Morton's Leam is relegated to a flood relief channel. (HEW 0823)

HOLME

C19. Holme Fen posts (TL 203894) are visual reminders of the shrinkage of the land due to improved drainage. The were installed near to Whittlesey Mere, one of the largest of the fenland meres and the last to be drained. Its size varied to some extent, but in 1786 it covered 1,570 acres. It lay in the course of the Old River Nene, which after leaving Peterborough made a large sweep to the south-west before turning back north-east through Ugg Mere and Ramsey Mere on its way to March and the sea.

As part of his major proposals for the drainage of the Middle and South Levels in 1777, John Golborne surveyed the mere and found it to be 4½ft deep. His estimate of £150,000 for all of the works was too large to contemplate, and none of them was done.

In 1837 Sir John Rennie was consulted about the drainage of the Middle and South Levels and proposed the usual remedy of a catchwater drain to divert the upland waters away from the Fens, which he then proposed could be drained satisfactorily to the (modern) River Nene. This was opposed by the Middle Level Corporation, who insisted on draining to the River Ouse. The main drain proposed by Walker & Burges would have started west of Whittlesey Mere and drained it, but the works were cut back to the eastern one-third when constructed in 1844-7 (**N26**), and the mere remained as it was.

In 1851 the proprietor of the land started work to drain the mere into Bevill's Leam and thence to the Middle Level Main Drain. The first step was to construct a northern

catchwater – the Black Ham River. Much of the mere was drained by gravity into this drain during 1851. Work on foundations for an engine house (TL 237903) started in March that year, and the engine drain was dug. By November an Appold steam-powered centrifugal pump of a type that had been exhibited at the Great Exhibition was installed – the first centrifugal pump to be put into use in Britain. A ceremonial start to its work was staged on 12 November and the remaining water was removed.

On 2 November 1852, heavy rains overpowered the pump and burst the bank of the drain. The area was flooded once more to a depth of three feet. However, once the rains had passed, the damage was made good and the pump was put to work continuously for three weeks, by which it gained the upper hand again and the land made suitable once more for arable.

Unfortunately, as elsewhere in the Fens, improved drainage caused the land to shrink, to the extent that by the 1890s there was almost no natural fall along the second-ary drains into the engine drain and the land became waterlogged for part of the year. In 1892 a new owner decided to cut a new drain to the north and install a second engine (TL 211903) to pump into the Black Ham. A matter of some debate at the time was the decision to use a scoop wheel – they had earlier been almost entirely superseded by pumps. It lasted only until 1913-14, when it was replaced by a centrifugal pump.

The Appold pump on the engine drain survived until 1877, and its fan is now in the Science Museum, South Kensington. Its replacement was itself superseded in 1924, but the present pump is electrically powered, installed in 1962. The original engine house has been completely demolished, and there are only small remains of the 1892 engine house.

When the Crystal Palace in London was being dismantled in 1852, one of its cast-iron columns was brought here and driven into the ground. Its top was fixed level with the peat surface while its base was firmly fixed on the Fen clay. The subsequent drop in the surrounding land demonstrates the effect of peat shrinkage when land drainage is undertaken. By 1860 4ft 10in of post was visible; by 1875 8ft 10in; and 1892 10ft. The level has continued to fall, although more slowly; originally about six feet above sea level, it is now about seven feet below. A second post was driven alongside in 1957 as the surface began to drop perilously close to the base of the original.

The posts are situated on the edge of the wood on the east side of the engine drain and can be approached by a bridge over Holme Lode. There is parking for three or four cars on the verge of the minor road that leads past the site. The mere itself was a short way further north. (HEW 0819)

110 *Houghton Watermill.*

HOUGHTON

C20. Houghton Mill (TL 281719) is a large water-mill with its machinery intact, showing how a substantial source of power could be provided before the advent of steam engines. It stands on a channel of the River Ouse midway between Huntingdon and St Ives, at a site where milling has taken place for over a thousand years. It existed already in A.D. 974 when it was recorded that part of the endowment of the Abbey of Ramsey, 10 miles away, was a meadow and mill at Houghton. It was also recorded in the Domesday Survey in 1086. Relationships between the villagers and the Abbey could be fraught. In 1500 the Abbot caused a weir to be built to maintain the level of water to drive the wheel. In times of heavy rain this obstruction to the flow of the river caused adjacent fields to be flooded, so the villagers destroyed it by main force. The Abbot issued a lawsuit against them, which went on until 1515 when the King's Court finally gave the villagers the right to open all the floodgates between Godmanchester and St Ives when their fields were in danger.

In 1539, when the monasteries were dissolved, the manor and mill were seized by the Crown, and remained in their possession until sold by King Charles I in 1625. It changed hands again in 1651, but was worked by a succession of tenants until 1930, when it was closed. It was purchased by a group of local residents, who gave it to the National Trust in 1939. It was used by the Youth Hostels Association until 1983, since when the National Trust has been restoring it as a working museum. The waterwheels were removed when the mill closed, in order once again to improve the river regime, and the Drainage Board installed sluices to control the flow; that on the south side still exists. Much of the machinery remained, however, and as a first step it was driven by an electric motor in order to demonstrate it at work. A new waterwheel was inserted on the north side of the mill in 1999, which powers one pair of millstones.

The present building is thought to have been built in the 17th century, but it was extensively altered in each of the two succeeding centuries. It has five storeys. Originally the roof was thatched. At one time the mill had a waterwheel on the north side and two on the south (the river runs east-west here). All were of the low breast shot type. The larger of the two southern wheels drove four pairs of millstones; the northern wheel, the second to be installed, powered three pairs of wheels and a dressing machine; the other southern wheel, upstream and in a different line from the earlier one, drove three pairs of stones, a sack hoist and a ventilation system. The wheels were respectively 17ft in diameter by 12ft wide, 14ft by 10ft and 13ft by seven feet. (HEW 1944)

HUNTINGDON

C21. Huntingdon Bridge (TL 242715) is a fine medieval bridge with a puzzling building history. It carries the Old North Road over the River Ouse. The roadway is just wide enough for two vehicles to pass each other, so a footbridge was built in 1965-6 on the upstream side. It rather spoils the view of the old bridge from that side but affords a good vantage point from which to inspect the fabric, which is the product of several phases of building. A bridge here almost certainly existed in Anglo-Saxon times, and was recorded in 1194. It was swept away in the hard winter of 1293-4 and the succeeding structure was described as ruinous several times during the 14th century, and major repairs were carried out in 1300, 1340 and 1370. In 1329 it was described as being 'in a ruinous state, in many places broken through, and at one part threatening to fall'; note that 'ruinous' did not imply that the bridge had collapsed. The arch nearest the town is lower and

111 Huntingdon Bridge, seen through the old timber railway viaduct in 1964, before the footbridge was erected alongside.

narrower than the others and is almost certainly the remains of the bridge that was swept away in 1293-4 or its immediate replacement. The second and third arches are flat-pointed, and have their western parapets carried by ornate trefoil brackets; the cutwaters between them are massive and triangular in plan. The fourth arch is known to have been broken down by Parliamentary forces in 1645 and replaced by a drawbridge, so this arch is later. The fifth arch is flat-pointed but without the elaborate decoration of the second and third arches, and the sixth arch is segmental. The form

112 *Lolham Bridges, Maxey.* of the piers differs too, the three southern ones being semi-hexagonal with dwarf cutwaters, the northern ones with cutwaters carried all the way up to the tops of the parapets. The Royal Commission on Ancient and Historic Monuments stated that the bridge was built *c.*1300 and suggested that it was the work of two different authorities, whose work met at the middle pier; it is known that the several hundreds of the county were responsible for its upkeep. It seems equally likely, however, that the present structure is the result of several partial rebuilds. (HEW 0064)

MAXEY

C22. Lolham Bridges (TF 111069 to TF 111074) carry unusual carved tablets recording their construction by the county. They lie on King Street, a secondary Roman route from London to Lincoln. The main Roman road from London to Lincoln crossed the River Nene at *Durobrivae* (near modern Water Newton) and continued north-west on higher ground past Stamford. From the Nene another Roman road, King Street, struck due north, crossing the Welland valley where it is lower and wider and then going on to rejoin the Ermine Street at Ancaster. The Welland crossing probably remained in use through Saxon and later times so that new bridges were required to cater for the increase of wheeled traffic in the 17th century.

Old bridges require regular maintenance and repair if they are to remain serviceable and at that time there was frequent argument about responsibility for this upkeep. If it could be shown that a landowner or his predecessors, or a parish or a hundred or other corporate body, had built or previously made repairs, or that it was principally of service to them, they would be held to have a continuing commitment. Only in the last resort, when no-one could be shown to be responsible and when the bridge was adjudged to be of use to the general public, would a county take over and repair it.

The present nine Lolham Bridges are moderate structures, of which five date back to the 17th or 18th century, with spans up to 16ft. The river formerly flowed in several channels but flood prevention works and extraction for water supply have drastically reduced the quantities passing here; several of the arches are now dry. King Street is now a local road only and the bridges have not been widened, so the road gives a good idea of the standards of 300 years ago.

Lolham Bridges lay within the Liberty of Peterborough and *c.*1669 they were disputing at the Midland Assizes their responsibility for some work to be done. Unusually, it seems that a general appeal was made to other counties, for there are receipts in Warwickshire County Record Office for monies spent on repairs at 'Lolam'. The Liberty had to raise £250 in 1674 to carry out their obligations. A panel on the south-western face of the south-western cutwater of bridge 8 is inscribed 'SUMPT COMI /TAT NORTH /AMPT 1641' and a similarly placed panel on bridge 7 states 'These Bridges are built / at ye Charge of ye whole / County / 1699'. It may well be that, in placing these tablets on the bridges, the authorities were trying to limit their liabilities to those structures alone. However, progress led inexorably to more and more bridges falling upon the county until the newly formed county councils in 1889 adopted almost every public highway bridge in their area. (HEW 1762)

PETERBOROUGH

C23. Peterborough Cathedral medieval crane is one of only three man-powered cranes to survive in Britain from the Middle Ages, though there are later examples at Berden and Harwich (**E9**) in Essex, Carisbrooke on the Isle of Wight, and Beverley Minster in the East Riding of Yorkshire. The medieval windlass cranes are at Peterborough Cathedral, Tewkesbury Abbey and Salisbury Cathedral. The first two are in towers built during the 12th century and the last in one of the 13th century. Peterborough is in the best state of preservation.

The building of the northern tower at the west end of Peterborough Cathedral began towards the end of the 12th century. In order to raise the stones it was necessary to have some sort of lifting machine. Ordinarily this would have been a gin or similar, placed at ground level and operated by a verne or treadwheel. Early treadwheels were operated by men inside the wheel, but from the 12th century greater leverage was obtained by having the men walk on rungs placed outside the wheel.

The barrel of the Peterborough crane measures 13in in diameter and with an effective length of 12ft is much the largest of the three. It is fitted with flanged iron end caps which, being only 10in diameter, necessitated reduction of the barrel to receive them. Journals 1½in in diameter protrude from the end caps. One end of the barrel is cut down to 12in square to receive the four rectangular spokes 7in by 4in which pass through and are secured to the barrel with wooden wedges; at the other end the spokes are attached to the rim with round dowels. The circular rim is 9ft 6in diameter and composed of scarfed and dowelled felloes. Twenty-two 1½in-diameter 'rungs', equally spaced, project equally on either side of the rim, on which the operators would 'climb'.

113 *Peterborough Cathedral medieval crane.*

Because of the style of attachment of the spokes to the barrel, this machine can be ascribed confidently to a date before the 16th century. Its carpentry is typical of millwork of the medieval period. It seems probable that it was installed during the first building of the tower and is therefore of the 12th century, although it should be noted that the spire above the tower is a 14th-century addition. (HEW 2698)

C24. Great Northern Railway Bridge (TL 191981) is one of the very few cast-iron underbridges to survive on a main line railway in Britain, though it has been strengthened to carry the much greater weight of modern trains. It was constructed for the Great Northern Railway main line from London via Peterborough to York and now carries the two up tracks of the East Coast Main Line of Network Rail across the River Nene in three equal spans of 66ft on the skew (approximately 54ft square).

114 *Nene Railway Bridge, Peterborough* (Illustrated London News, 1850).

Each span has six ribs each with a rise of 8ft 6in and a radius of 62ft 6in. These are I-sections one foot wide by 2ft 6in deep, of approximately 1½in thickness, cast in halves, bolted together at the crown and to the bearing blocks. Spacing of the ribs is 3ft 6in, 6ft 9in, 3ft 6in, 6ft 9in, 3ft 6in; the width between parapets is 24ft. The open work cast-iron spandrels support cast-iron plates carrying ballasted track. Each pier has 12 cast-iron, 10ft-high, fluted pillars built off a 37ft 6in by 6ft 6in iron caisson in the river. The masonry abutments once contained arches, which have been filled in with the more recent construction of bridges on either side.

The railway was designed by Joseph Cubitt, with his father (Sir) William Cubitt as consulting engineer. The main contractor was Thomas Brassey, but the bridge was almost certainly built under a subcontract by Fox, Henderson & Co. The bridge was strengthened in 1910-11 by bracing between the ribs and between the abutments. In 1924 a truss bridge was erected alongside it on the west to carry the down lines. Public footpaths along the banks of the river enable close inspection of the structure, though it should be noted that the sign attributing its design to Lewis Cubitt is not correct. (HEW 0093)

There was a similar bridge on the same railway over the River Ouse at Huntingdon. It was replaced by steel girders in the 1930s.

115 *Tracked Hovercraft at Railworld, Peterborough.*

C25. Tracked Hovercraft was a project of the 1960s to create a high-speed railway using the hovering principle. From 1969 a purpose-built, full-scale track was constructed beside the Old Bedford River (**C13**) north from Earith on which a prototype vehicle could be tested. Any practical application would run on an elevated structure, so because of the high speeds and large forces involved, the prestressed concrete beams needed to be precast to very high standards. Unfortunately neither Government nor private industry was willing to commit further funding beyond the initial tranche and work stopped in 1973; the whole structure was demolished in 1974. A section of track and a prototype vehicle can be seen at Railworld Museum in Peterborough. (HEW 2660)

REACH

C26. Reach Lode is one of four man-made water-courses or lodes that run from the fen edge in north-east Cambridgeshire to the River Cam and are known to have existed in medieval times; the other three are Bottisham, Swaffham Bulbeck and Burwell Lodes. They each take a generally north-westerly direction over the fen and cut across the natural drainage of the area, which is northerly/north-easterly. All are raised on an embankment above the level of the surrounding fen and have wharves and hythes at their south-eastern end.

Traditionally the lodes have been said to have been constructed by the Romans, for drainage and transport. Trade at Reach is recorded from 1125 onwards and an annual fair was **116** *The Hythe,* appropriated to the town of Cambridge by a charter of 1201. Goods were transported *Reach.* to and from the Hythe (TL 56506640), a man-made platform of rammed chalk, which splits the Lode into several basins (TL 56546641). In medieval times the Lode was much used for transporting clunch, a chalky stone, from quarries at TL 565658.

Roman remains have been found alongside Reach Lode, but none of much significance at the landward end. Recent opinion, noting the lack of any hard evidence for a Roman origin, has suggested instead that they may be late-Saxon and constructed for water management by monasteries with estates in the area. Reach Lode is fed at its 'upper' end by a catchwater drain and the Lode could have been constructed to conduct the upland water past the fen, with rainwater from the fen being conducted in a smaller drain alongside.

Since medieval times, the fen has been drained, leading to a lowering of ground level as the ground dried out, and the embankment in which the Lode runs has been built up in order to maintain the flow to the River Cam. As part of the improvements to the River Great Ouse at the time of the Eau Brink Cut, a lock into the river Cam at Upware was built in 1821.

St IVES

C27. St Ives Bridge (TL 312711) has a bridge chapel built over one of its cutwaters. It is a six-arch bridge over the River Great Ouse, of which the northern four arches are original. A timber bridge was built by the Abbey of Ramsey to bring travellers to the abbey's great fair; the new market place moved the centre of the town away from the parish **117** *St Ives Bridge.* church, which lies some way to the west. Ramsey was one of the fenland abbeys that had rights to quarry stone at Barnack, near Stamford. The present stone bridge was built with this, presumably brought to the site on barges, and was completed in 1426, when the Abbot dedicated the chapel on the bridge to St Leger. The southern arch was taken down and replaced by a drawbridge in 1645 during the Civil War, and it and the next adjacent arch were rebuilt in 1716. These two are segmental arches, but the four northern ones are pointed, with five chamfered ribs beneath each. (HEW 0062)

The southern approach is along a causeway of 55 arches over the flood meadows, built in 1822, and known as New Bridge. Arched causeways of this kind are unusual, particularly for vehicular traffic. Probably the finest medieval example remaining is Stanton Causeway, which connects Swarkestone Bridge over the River Trent in Derbyshire to the higher ground to the south. The nearest example to St Ives is the southern approach to **Huntingdon Bridge (C21)**, a long embankment that was pierced by two eight-arch bridges, of which only one remains. There are also causeways further up the River Great Ouse at Bromham and Tempsford, both in Bedfordshire.

STRETHAM

C28. Stretham Pumping Station (TL 517730) is the oldest remaining steam engine in the Fens. A series of very wet years in the 1720s severely strained the finances of the Bedford Level Corporation, the statutory drainage authority for the fens, so that it was unable to exercise its functions effectively. This led to demands from local areas for autonomy so that they might undertake these responsibilities themselves. Haddenham was the first area to separate, by an Act of 1727; another was created in 1738, and the Waterbeach Level was the third to do so, in 1741.

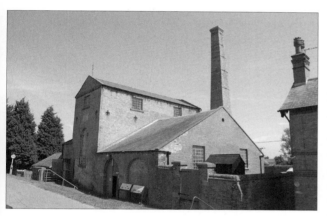

Power to raise water from low-lying areas into the main rivers, and so away to the sea, was provided at first by windmills, but these were often unable to work when most needed, in times of flood, due to lack of wind. Agricultural improvements during the Napoleonic Wars both provided the capital and emphasised the need for more reliable power sources. Steam engines had been used in the Netherlands since 1785 and one was suggested for Middle Fen in 1789. One was used to pump out the foundations of the Hobhole Sluice, under construction in 1804 as part of the East, West and Wildmore Fens works

118 *Stretham Pumping Station.*

in Lincolnshire. John Rennie senior, who had been Engineer for those works, reported in 1814 on the Waterbeach Level. He recommended a catchwater drain to keep the 'highland' waters out of the Level, and a steam engine near Harimeer Corner, where the River Cam joins the Old West River. The commissioners were appalled by the estimated cost and Rennie's proposals were not carried out.

The first permanent steam engine in the fens was erected at Sutton St Edmund in 1817. By 1830 there were 13 engines at work, of which several had been provided by the Butterley Company of Derbyshire, whose engineer was Joseph Glynn. The abolition of the tax on sea-borne coal in 1831 greatly improved the economics of steam engines and in that year the Waterbeach Level Commissioners decided to go ahead. A site at Stretham, further up the Old West River, was chosen, where there was a hard bed of gravel about 10ft below the surface that would provide good foundations for the engine without the need for piling. The engine house was built for £2,050 by a Mr Briggs of West Ferry, Lincolnshire, and an engine of 60hp by Butterley was installed for £2,900. It is now the oldest steam engine surviving in the fens.

Its cylinder was 39in by 96in, with steam supplied at 4psi by two boilers. The engine drove a scoop wheel 29ft in diameter by three feet wide; in 1850, shrinking in the Level necessitated its being altered to 33ft by 2½ft. It was again rebuilt in 1896 to its present 37ft 2in by 2ft 4¼in. The boiler house was extended in 1846/7 to accommodate a third boiler, and the boilers were replaced in 1871 and 1878, all the new ones being supplied by Butterley.

The engine was put on standby in 1924 when it was superseded by a diesel engine in a separate building beside the old engine house. It was last used in March 1941. After a period of neglect, a trust was formed in 1959 to restore it and open it to the public occasionally. As the boilers are no longer safe to use, an electric motor now drives the machinery.

The Stretham Engine Trust maintains a website http://strethamoldengine.org.uk, that gives details of times when the site is open to the public. (HEW 0219)

SWAFFHAM

C29. Devil's Ditch is a massive earthwork 7½ miles long running in three straight alignments, 1½, five and one mile long north-west from Stetchworth to meet **Reach Lode (C26)** at Reach. Together, they form a barrier more than 10 miles long. Although not the longest such earthwork in Britain, it is the largest. Its date has not been established with certainty, nor has its purpose. The most common suggestions are that it was constructed in the seventh century to defend East Anglia from attack from the south-west side at a time when warfare between tribes and kingdoms was common. Excavations in 1924 found Roman and Romano-British pottery fragments under the bank, thus dating it no earlier than that period.

The ditch when dug was 4.87 m deep, 13m wide at original ground level and seven metres wide at its bottom, with side slopes at 32-6° from the horizontal. The soil was thrown up to form a bank 20m wide at its base, and is now about 4.5m high. Over time erosion from the sides of the bank (or vallum) has caused the bottom of the ditch (or fosse) to fill to some extent, thus reducing the apparent height. In more peaceable times short lengths of the bank have been removed to allow the construction of south-west to north-east roads, and in places the bank has been quarried for road-surfacing materials. (HEW 2707)

119 *Devil's Ditch, near Reach.*

C30. Swaffham & Bottisham Fen (TL 56) has been subjected to several major changes in its drainage over the last 2,000 years. It is an area of low-lying land about six miles long by three miles wide and comprising about 7,000 acres. It stretches from Horningsea in the south to Upware in the north and is bounded on its north-west side by the River Cam and on its south-east by a low ridge on which stand the villages of Swaffham Prior, Swaffham Bulbeck and Bottisham. It has seen an unusual number of man-made changes in the basic pattern of its drainage.

In earliest times, the natural drainage was broadly as described by G. Fowler (*Cambridgeshire Archaeological Society Proceedings*, 33 (1933), pp.108-16), when the main stream flowed south-west to north-east, then turned north-west to join the River Cam at Upware. Three (Bottisham, Swaffham Bulbeck and Reach) lodes, more or less parallel with each other and going south-east to north-west, were constructed at an early date; they are usually said to be Roman and may well be so, though the evidence is not conclusive. Reach Lode was mentioned in the late 11th century. All of these cut across

120
*Commissioners'
Drain, Swaffham
and Bottisham Fen.*

and destroyed the natural drainage; the original main stream was diverted into each lode. The lodes were used mainly for navigation, and there is no evidence now of large-scale drainage works being undertaken in the medieval period (though Quy Water may be medieval).

In the 17th century, following the campaign of drainage of the Bedford Level, 95,000 acres of land were allocated to the Adventurers (subsequently the Bedford Level Corporation) in recompense for their efforts. Of this land, 2,600 acres were in these fens, and in Burwell Fen immediately north. These lands, when they were laid out in 1655-6, were chosen to be the most easy to drain. They lay much along the line of the original main stream in the centre of the fens and were drained by an artificial cut, which passed under Bottisham and Swaffham Bulbeck Lodes by culverts and then into Reach Lode and the River Cam. During the rest of the century the lands not owned by the Bedford Level Corporation began to be enclosed by the local landowners. As elsewhere in the Fens, peat shrinkage started to affect Bottisham and Swaffham Fens, so by 1719 a windpump had been erected at Upware, where Reach Lode met the Cam, by the BLC and the landowners to deal with this. Continuing problems with drainage led to a movement by some landowners to set up a local drainage commission independent of the BLC. It was resisted by owners in Burwell Fen, whose lands also drained into the Cam via Reach Lode, and whose valuable peat turbaries would be badly affected, so the Swaffham and Bottisham people went ahead by themselves; their Drainage Commission was established by an Act in 1767.

The first action of the new commissioners was to recut Reach Old Lode. Because the windpump at Upware was not adequate to the task, a new drain, still called the Mill Drain, was cut and another windpump was erected at Bottisham Mill; it was working by 1770. Bottisham and Swaffham Bulbeck were enclosed in 1800-1, and a windpump installed at Swaffham Upper Mill. The overall result was to return the drainage to a south-east to north-west axis, as it had been during the medieval period.

Part of the Eau Brink scheme carried out in 1819-21 (**N25**) required dredging and regrading of the River Cam up to Clayhithe. It was acknowledged that these works would cause increased seepage through the river banks into the Bottisham and Swaffham Fens, so the Eau Brink Commissioners agreed, as they were required to by their Act, to make a contribution towards improved drainage of the fens back into the river. John Rennie, who was the Engineer of the Eau Brink Cut, was consulted and he sent Richard Grantham to survey the area. Grantham was delayed by bad weather, but wished to spend a further few days to take levels down to Ely where a drainage by gravity might be effected. The sketch of his proposals still exists among Rennie's papers in the National Library of Scotland. Rennie thought that it would be necessary to go even further, at least to Denver Sluice, in fact, for a natural drainage so in February 1820 he recommended a new drain, from Quy in the south west to just short of Reach Lode in the north east and then parallel to the Lode to a separate engine at Upware; it was straighter than and to the east of the earlier Adventurers' drain, with a gradient of 3½in to the mile and, like it, passed under the two southern lodes. These works were carried out, as Rennie had suggested, by Jolliffe & Banks, who were also the contractors for the main Eau Brink works. The engine at Upware was only the fourth steam engine to be erected in the Fens (but not the first, as claimed by his son Sir John Rennie in his *Autobiography*). The commissioners, however, had not constructed the catchwater drain that would have prevented the upland waters from coming down into the fens, so the 24hp engine that Rennie recommended was underpowered for the larger work required. It was replaced by one of 70hp in 1850, which was sufficiently powerful to drain the whole of the fens, and the drains in the south were once more turned to the north east. Continued shrinkage required its scoop wheel to be 36ft in diameter, compared with 26ft of the 1821 engine, and it continued to keep the fens drained until replaced by diesel in 1927, though it remained on standby for another 10 years. The buildings were demolished in 1939. (HEW 2700)

THORNEY

C31. Thorney Tankyard (TF 283044) is remarkable as an enlightened and probably the earliest example of a complete provision of mains water and sewerage to an estate village. The village was designed for the Duke of Bedford, a major landowner in the Fens, by the architect S.S. Teulon in a style less aggressively Gothic than most of his buildings, and the Tankyard is of a piece with the rest of the village. The works themselves, though, were designed by John Hodgson Jones, an engineer who later had an extensive practice in this field. Work started in 1852 and was completed within three years, at a cost of £22,446. The foundation of the tower is 18ft deep; the tower 74ft high and the chimney 89ft. Water was taken from Thorney River and pumped to the cast-iron tank at the top of the tower by two beam engines of 12hp supplied by Neilson of Glasgow, which also operated the sawmills and carpenter's shop. Sewerage drained to the tankyard by gravity, and was then pumped up to another tank, from which it was distributed over the allotments north-east of the village. The engines were removed in the 1930s when mains connection was made. The tower is a prominent landmark from the bypass and the village museum in the Bedford Hall below the tower, off Station Road, is open on some Sunday afternoons. (HEW 1172)

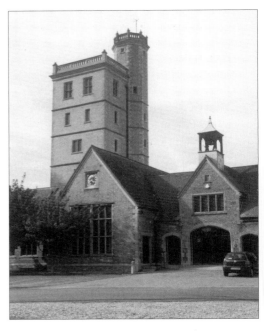

121 *Thorney Tankyard.*

TYDD

C32. North Level Main Drain (TF 505002 to TF 588142) was a major improvement to the drainage of the northern third of the Fens. It was the successor to the medieval system by which the North Level of the Fens drained via the Old South Eau to Cloughs Cross and thence by the Shire Drain to Gunthorpe Sluice into the River Nene. The line of these drains was very sinuous and that they are very old is shown by the fact that they formed (and in large part still do form) the county boundary between Cambridgeshire and Lincolnshire. In the early 1630s the New South Eau was dug in a straight line between Nene Terrace near Crowland and Cloughs Cross but the Shire Drain remained unimproved. In 1828 a local engineer, Thomas Pear II reported on his survey for a new main drain from Cloughs Cross to Gunthorpe Sluice to replace the Shire Drain. The new line would be 8¼ miles long, compared with 12 miles by the older drain. The Act was obtained in 1829; Thomas Telford was appointed consultant and work started. Pear and William Swansborough, another local engineer, supervised the work. It was completed in 1834. A sluice (see below) was built on a new site adjacent to the Nene Outfall. A new

bridge, with two openings each for the north and south arms of the South Eau and sluice gates to control the flow through, was erected at Cloughs Cross. The Drain was dug deep enough to allow navigation by barges and landing stages formed part of the bridge complex there.

The completion of the drain made possible a drainage by gravity in the Level for the first time in a hundred years, at a time when the rest of the fens relied on windpumps and steam engines. Its success can be gauged by the oft-quoted statement by Tycho Wing, agent to the Duke

122 *North Level Main Drain, Cloughs Cross Bridge, wharves and sluices.*

of Bedford and a substantial landowner in his own right, that 'in the winter of 1836 we actually saw the water moving in the Wryde Drain at Thorney which no man had seen before'. Thorney is about nine miles above Cloughs Cross as the local drains flow. (HEW 2654)

C33. Tydd Protection Sluice (TF 462179) was built using innovative construction techniques. It was a reaction to the floods in the South Holland District caused by the failure of its sluice in 1851, and in the Middle Level by the failure of its sluice in 1862. Problems with the North Level Outfall Sluice in 1866 (see above) and again in 1868 resolved the North Level Commissioners to erect a 'Protection Sluice' shortly upstream so that if the outer one gave way, the Level would not suffer the same fate as the other two.

The Protection Sluice was designed by Benjamin Stockman, who had already dealt with the problems in 1866 and 1868. The novel feature of his scheme was to install the sluice in the North Level Drain, about a quarter of a mile upstream from the Outfall Sluice, without stopping the drainage. This was effected, instead of using the traditional method of timber piles driven into the sand, by fabricating 34 rectangular caissons of

123 *Tydd Pumping Station, formerly Protection Sluice.*

boiler-plate iron, each about 9ft by 3ft 6in by 23ft deep and sinking them until their tops were 2ft 6in below the bed of the drain, in two rows across it, and one under each pier. Great difficulty was experienced at first in lowering the caissons, despite the use of 50-70 tons of kentledge to weigh them down. While excavating inside the caissons to assist in their sinking, the sand beneath welled up and filled the caisson again. However, one of the contractor's draughtsmen modified an American invention, known today as a grab, and by using them in conjunction with a portable steam engine enabled the works to make progress. The caissons were then filled with concrete and the spaces between them excavated and also filled with concrete. This created a base of concrete 120ft by 60ft by 23ft deep on which concrete-filled cast-iron piers, sluice gates and a roadway were erected. When the sluice was tested in February 1872 by letting in a high tide, seepage was experienced around the brick-built abutments. The wings were re-excavated and rebuilt. The contract for the caissons was worth £10,800. The problem with the seepage led to a Chancery Court case which the contractor lost. The total cost of the works might have amounted to about £15,000.

In 1936 lowering of the ground surface upstream (due to improved drainage) and lack of maintenance of the drain caused severe floods and E.C. Farran of Doncaster was commissioned to report. He concluded that it was no longer possible to drain the North Level by gravity alone and recommended pumping stations at four places, including Tydd Protection Sluice. The sluice was partially embanked and the pumping station was completed in 1938. (HEW 2655)

WANSFORD

C34. New Bridge (TL 076994) has the largest span of any mass concrete bridge in Britain. It has three spans of 50ft, 109ft 6in and 50ft; each rises 15ft. It was designed by Sir Owen Williams and was a development of his bridge over the River Spey on the upgraded A9 Perth to Inverness road; the mass concrete bridge over Great Miami River, Sidney, Ohio (1922-4) may also have been an influence.

When the rise:span ratio is greater than 1:7, the volume of concrete in a mass concrete bridge is about twice that in a reinforced concrete one. At Wansford, the availability of aggregates in a pit beside the bridge site and the distance from supplies of steel reinforcement meant that savings on the latter were greater than the cost of the extra volume of concrete. The foundations of the bridge are on blue lias clay, which is subject to settlement when loaded, so the structure was built with three temporary steel hinges across its width to allow relative movement as settlement took place. When this had ceased, the hinges were filled with concrete to make the structure continuous. The spandrels and decks were cast *in situ* as a series of separate blocks to allow for shrinkage during the curing process; when this had finished, keyways were filled with a rich concrete. The exposed surfaces of the bridge were bush-hammered to expose the aggregate and so give a finish in keeping with its surroundings. It is still obviously a concrete structure but the finish has weathered well over time.

124 *New Bridge, Wansford.*

The contract for construction was let in August 1926. The names of the two counties which the bridge united then – Huntingdonshire and the Soke of Peterborough – are cast on each face, as is the date 'MCMXXVIII'. The bridge however was only ready for testing on 8 March 1929 and was opened formally on 22 March 1929. (HEW 2697)

C35. Old Bridge (TL 074992) is a 12-arch bridge over the River Nene that formerly carried the Great North Road. It is interesting as it shows clearly the three distinct phases of its construction and rebuilding. A bridge existed in 1221 when an indulgence was granted for its repair; it then had eight spans. It was presumably then of timber, as it was repaired with oak in 1234. It was again repaired by the vill of Wansford (on the north bank – the main part of the village now known as Wansford on the south

125 *Old Bridge,*
       Wansford.

bank is in the parish of Stibbington) in the 14th century, when pontage was granted. Three arches were destroyed in 1571 and rebuilt in 1577, apparently with four adjacent arches. In 1586 the shire of Northampton was responsible for the bridge. Three arches were rebuilt in 1672-4, and when two arches were damaged by ice in February 1792 the opportunity was taken to reduce the risk and also to improve the navigation by replacing them with one, larger arch, the present number 2 (numbered from the right or southern bank).

Arches 12 to 6 appear to be of the rebuilding of 1577 – the date appears on the inside of the eastern, downstream, parapet between arches 6 and 5; these seven arches are much lower than the others and the superstructure has been raised to suit the latter. Arches 5 to 3 are of 1672-4; arch 2 is dated '1795' and arch 1 is of one of the earlier builds, now masked by widening. Arches 12 to 10 have two arch rings; arches 9 to 6 have three, of which the lowest is a later strengthening; arches 5 to 3 have one. Arch 2 is elliptical; the others are semi-circular. The 1577 portion is 13ft 4in wide between parapets, 16ft overall; arch 2 (1795) is 30ft wide overall; arch 1 was 20ft 11in wide originally, but now widened by 11ft 3in.

The former county boundary (Huntingdonshire and the Soke of Peterborough), now Cambridgeshire and Peterborough unitary authority, is shown by a triangular cast-iron marker between arches 6 and 5. The different phases of construction can best be seen from the footpath that leads west from the north end of the bridge. A closer view can be had from the south-western corner. (HEW 0051)

WATERBEACH

C36. Car Dyke in Cambridgeshire is one of two artificial watercourses built by the Romans which have subsequently been given the same name. No trace has been found of a link between the two. The purpose of the Lincolnshire Car Dyke has been the subject of debate in modern times. Because excavation has shown that it was not absolutely continuous, the more commonly accepted theory now is that it was a catchwater drain to direct rainwater flowing off the higher ground to the south and east, away from the fens. The suggestion that it was intended as a canal to transport grain from East Anglia to the garrisons in Lincoln and the north is now generally discounted, though proponents of this idea claim that the Dyke is not ideally situated to be a catchwater either. A length of the Lincolnshire Car Dyke exists north of Peterborough. It joined the Rivers Nene and Welland and surveys have shown that its bed fell by more than ten feet from the watershed down to each river.

The Cambridgeshire Car Dyke linked the River Cam with the West Water and probably was used for navigation, though it is hard to understand why the Romans should have expended such a considerable effort for what was no more than a short cut between two rivers that united further downstream. It is a series of straight sections, about eight kilometres long in all. The length at Waterbeach is the only clear stretch of the Cambridgeshire Car Dyke remaining. Excavations have shown that it was 45ft wide at the top, seven feet deep and 28ft wide at the bottom. Sherds of pottery have been unearthed that show that it was constructed possibly as early as A.D. 50/60 and certainly by the early second century, and continued in use at least until the fourth century. (HEW 0822)

126 *Wicken Fen Windpump.*

WICKEN

C37. Wicken Fen Windpump (TL 560708) is the sole survivor of the many windpumps that lifted water out of the fen drains into the main rivers to flow away. Originally built to drain the adjoining Adventurers' Fen, it was in a derelict condition when it was moved a third of a mile to its present position on Wicken Sedge Fen in 1956. It was heavily restored, but using the original ironwork, and is now in running order. Rather than its original role, it is used periodically to raise water from the drain into the dykes that maintain the sedge fen. It is a small smock mill with four 30ft-diameter sails, which drive a scoop wheel of 13ft diameter. Its optimum lift is only two feet, though it can raise through double that height if necessary. The site is owned by the National Trust and a charge is made to non-members for admission to the fen. (HEW 0689)

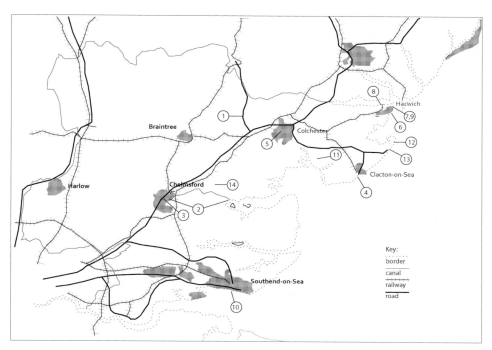

Map of Essex.

E1. Chappel Viaduct
E2. Chelmer & Blackwater Navigation
E3. Moulsham Bridge
E4. Clacton Pier
E5. Colchester Water Tower
E6. Dovercourt Leading Lights
E7. Harwich Lighthouses
E8. Parkeston Quay, Harwich
E9. Treadmill Crane, Harwich
E10. Southend Pier
E11. Thorrington Tidemill
E12. Naze Tower
E13. Walton Pier
E14. Wickham Bishops Viaduct

CHAPPEL

E1. Chappel Viaduct (TL 896284) is the largest railway viaduct in East Anglia. It was designed by Peter Bruff and built by George Wythes in 1847-9 at a cost of £21,000 as part of the works for the Colchester, Stour Valley, Sudbury & Halstead Railway. The viaduct bears an unusually large commemorative tablet on pier no. 21 (numbered from the south end) marking the start of construction. The company only ever built between Marks Tey and Sudbury (and a short branch in Colchester), and the railway was opened on 2 July 1849. Other companies later extended the line, which then formed part of a wide system of railways serving the Essex and Suffolk border area, but it once again stops at Sudbury.

The viaduct is of brick, with 32 six-ring semi-circular arches, each of 30ft clear span, to carry the railway across the valley of the River Colne and the A604 road. The structure is 1,136ft long and straight throughout, with a 1 in 120 gradient rising northwards. The piers taper upwards in both planes and are 7ft 1in wide at the base, 4ft 11in wide at the springing of the arches and have a six-foot-wide central opening, arched top and bottom. The maximum height of the viaduct is 74ft from river to parapets (70ft to rail level). The structure contains seven million bricks, made by the contractor at a brickworks he set up less than a mile from the site. The somewhat austere appearance of the viaduct is relieved by rib courses at the extrados of the arches, corbelled imposts below arch-springing level and interesting slotted piers. The Engineer, Peter Bruff, read a paper to the Institution of Civil Engineers on 26 March 1850 describing the viaduct, in which he stated that cost had influenced his preference for building the arches in brick rather than laminated timber as originally intended. In the discussion which followed the paper, I.K. Brunel firmly opposed the view that there was a cost advantage of brick compared with timber spans. (HEW 0593)

CHELMSFORD

E2. Chelmer & Blackwater Navigation (TL 713066 to TL 871068) was designed by John Rennie senior. The first proposal for creating a navigation along the River Chelmer had been put forward in 1677 by Andrew Yarranton, in his book *England's Improvement by Sea and Land*. Because of opposition from the town of Maldon, the port on the estuary

127 *(Left) Chappel Viaduct, piers.*

128 *(Right) Chelmer & Blackwater Navigation.*

of the river, nothing came of this. In 1733 another well-known river engineer, John Hore, proposed two schemes, one of which was for a canal on a new line, but this, too, was defeated. In 1762 the idea was revived and John Smeaton and Thomas Yeoman, two of the foremost engineers of the day, each undertook a survey. After Yeoman's survey had been checked by Ferdinando and William Stratford – Ferdinando died as a result of malaria caught during his survey – an Act was passed on 6 June 1766 for making the river navigable from Maldon to Chelmsford. Unfortunately, insufficient money could be raised to allow work to start, in compliance with a clause in the Act, and this scheme also lapsed.

Interest revived during the canal mania of the early 1790s and on 6 September 1792 John Rennie senior, with a colleague called Charles Wedge, started to survey the river once more. Rennie, who earlier that year had obtained an Act for the Lancaster Canal and was also working on the Ipswich & Stowmarket Navigation (**S11**) as well as survey-ing for a proposed Rochdale Canal, presented his report on 6 December. He preferred improving the river to building a canal because the former would use less water and would allow greater access to the river for farmers' livestock, as well as draining the meadows and easing the passage of floods. This last would prove ironical in the outcome. There would be artificial cuts to bypass the mills on the river and one for the last half-mile into the terminal basin at Springfield, Chelmsford. The last 2½ miles below Beeleigh would avoid Maldon altogether and terminate at a new site on Colliers Reach in the Blackwater estuary, now known as Heybridge Basin. After a second survey by Matthew Hall in 1793, the bill received royal assent on 17 June 1793.

Rennie was appointed Engineer to the navigation and set about finding a resident engineer to be appointed by the company and direct the work. Fortunately, in a year when no less than 32 canals received Acts of Parliament, work on the Ipswich & Stow-market Navigation was coming rapidly to a close and Rennie approached his resident engineer, Richard Coates, there. Coates accepted on 13 August and on 16 August Rennie replied, giving him instructions on how to set about the business.

Work started between Beeleigh and Hoemill and by April 1795 work was in hand from Heybridge up to Paper Mill Lock at Little Baddow. Already there had been problems with flood damage at the complicated junction at Beeleigh, where a mill existed and the River Blackwater and a private canal called the Langford Cut joined the River Chelmer. This was overcome by a cut to bypass the mill, locking down into the Blackwater, providing a weir there to discharge excess water back into the river and continuing the navigation down through another lock on its way to Heybridge. On 23 April 1796 the first shipload of coal bound for Chelmsford progressed up as far as Little Baddow, whence it completed its journey by road. The final length to the Springfield Basin was opened on 3 June 1797.

In December 1797 there was serious flooding, causing shoals that obstructed the waterway, a problem that recurred with each heavy rainfall. By March 1799 the company asked Lord Petre to meet Rennie and request him to survey the line and propose a remedy at no cost to the company. Rennie, in his reply, pointed out that he had not personally laid out the canal and although he declined to undertake the works at his own expense, he did make another survey gratis. Problems with the condition of the locks continued and Rennie was again called in in 1805. The works he recommended then were directed by his assistant, James Green, who would later become the first county surveyor of Devon. Despite the problems, the canal was successful both in terms of the economy of the area and in giving its shareholders dividends of about three per cent p.a., at least until the advent of railways. The first boatload of coal had been supplied by Messrs Bryde & Coates, and after 1799 Richard Coates became a successful coal and timber merchant in Chelmsford, making good use of the navigation.

The navigation is 14 miles long and has 13 locks. It was a broad one, designed to take barges measuring 60ft long by 16ft wide. The barges were flat bottomed, and it was said that the navigation was the shallowest of any in the country on which commercial traffic was carried regularly. The sea lock at Heybridge has been lengthened to take vessels 107ft by 26ft, drawing eight feet at neap tides. The management of the waterway was taken over in 2005 by a branch of the Inland Waterways Association, and the navigation remains open for leisure traffic. (HEW 2711)

E3. Moulsham Bridge (TL 710065) is the only stone bridge designed by the notable architect and county surveyor of Essex, John Johnson. Also called Stone Bridge, it is situated in the heart of Chelmsford and carries the original main road over the River Can, half a mile above its confluence with the River Chelmer. The bridge has a single segmental arch of 35ft 9in span in Portland stone with the west keystone inscribed '1787' and attractive balusters in terracotta. In fact it was opened in 1788. Of interest are the decorative stone paterae, bearing effigies of river gods, set in the spandrels. The abutments are founded on timber piles with tiled cap courses thought to be Norman. There is a marked hump over the bridge, which had a 20ft-wide roadway and two footpaths each five feet wide; now it has been pedestrianised. The bridge was scheduled as an Ancient Monument in 1958 and listed as a Building of Architectural & Historical Interest in 1968.

The first bridge was built just upstream of a ford in 1100, in the reign of Henry I, by Morris, Bishop of London. Chelmsford was then a small settlement of five cottages but it grew in size and in 1199 was granted a market by King John. The second bridge was constructed on the same site in the mid-14th century by Ralph, Bishop of London, the work being carried out by Henry de Yevele who also built the nave of Westminster Abbey. The medieval bridge had three Gothic-style arches with two piers in the river. This was the London to Colchester road and it appears that the narrow bridge became congested with traffic because a timber footway was built on the west side about 1520. When the present bridge was constructed in 1785-8, the two piers of the medieval bridge were left in the river and were later suspected of causing serious flooding in the town. Thomas Telford was consulted in 1824 and recommended deepening the river and cleaning its

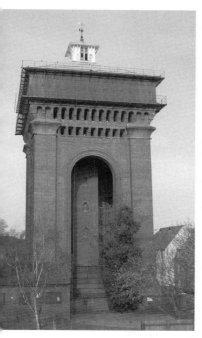

130 *Balkerne Hill Water Tower, Colchester.*

131 *Dovercourt Low Lighthouse, seen beyond the legs of the High Lighthouse.*

course, which led to the removal of the redundant piers. The river banks are now concreted through the town. (HEW 1368)

CLACTON-ON-SEA

E4. Clacton Pier (TM 177145) was built by Peter Bruff, the Ipswich-based engineer who had purchased 50 acres of land in 1865 to develop the small fishing village into a coastal resort. The following year he obtained an Act of Parliament to build a pier. Unable at first to do much because of financial problems, he struck a deal with the Woolwich Steam Packet Company that enabled him to build a memel timber landing stage 480ft long in 1870-1, just within the time allowed by the Act. Sea trips to Clacton proved popular and visitor facilities were added by degrees. In 1893 an extension of the pier to 1,180ft was designed by Walter Kinipple. In plan the pier now has three distinct sections – at the shore end, a later oblong area 100 yards wide and said to cover five acres provides space for a vast amusement arcade; an ovoid shape 85 yards across at the seaward end is joined to it by the 20yd-wide stem of the pier. The timber piles have been replaced by concrete; the deck at the shore end is concrete and the remainder is timber. At the pier head a landing berth extends northward at a flat angle. This projection is on timber piles with a concrete deck nine yards wide and three feet below the general level of the main pier. The lifeboat house is on an extension of the pier structure on the north side. (HEW 1658)

COLCHESTER

E5. Colchester Water Tower (TL 993252) on Balkerne Hill has been one of the most distinctive features of the town skyline since 1883 and since that time it has changed from being an object of public controversy to one of civic affection, with the local name of 'Jumbo'. The name was applied in scorn at the time, using the nickname of an elephant in London Zoo which had become a national celebrity because of its sale to Phineas Barnum, the great showman.

In the late 1850s, Peter Bruff, the railway engineer, drilled an artesian well on the site and made some improvement in the deficient water main system, but it was still inadequate for the expanding town and the council took over when the 1875 Public Health Act made local authorities responsible for water supply. James Wicks, a leading town councillor, advocated building a water tower on the high ground near the town centre to provide a gravity-fed supply and this solution was adopted despite much local opposition.

The tower was built by Henry Everett & Son, an Essex firm of builders, to a design by Charles Clegg, the Borough Surveyor and Engineer. The red brick tower is 88ft 5in high from ground level to the base of the tank and more than a million bricks were used in its construction. There is a high arched opening faced with Corsehill stone on each side of the tower, and there is decorative arched crenellation at the top. A central shaft carries the rising and supply mains. The tank, made of cast-iron plates cross-tied with heavy iron bars, was supplied by A.G. Mumford. It is 55ft 7in square by 12ft deep and can hold 221,000 gallons. The roof is surmounted by a wooden cupola and at a height of 131ft 5in the tower dwarfs the surrounding buildings. The total cost including the service mains amounted to £11,138. Exterior walkways at the bottom and top levels of the tank were added in 1908. Originally, the roof of the tank was tiled but this was changed in 1948 to copper-sheet cladding overlaying felted boarding. Today the borough water comes from distant reservoirs and Jumbo is used as a balancing tank for the daily peak periods. (HEW 1688)

DOVERCOURT

E6. Dovercourt Leading Lights (TM 253308) are rare survivals of a type of lighthouse that was once more common. The most prominent landmarks on the Dovercourt seafront are two navigation light towers, one close to the concrete sea wall and the other some 200 yards to seaward in a line almost east-west, connected by a rock causeway that is submerged at high tide. They were built to guide ships into the harbour at Harwich, replacing the lighthouses at Harwich itself (**E7**), which no longer served as leading lights after the channel was altered by the construction of the Harwich Breakwater. The new leading lights, when brought into line, gave a bearing clear of the Landguard Point shoal and they superseded the Harwich lights on November 1863.

The towers are thought to have been designed by James Walker, consulting engineer to Trinity House, using for their foundation iron screw piles, an invention of Alexander Mitchell patented in 1830. The High Tower (inshore) is 56ft high with a six-sided lantern room, 12ft 6in wide by nine feet high. The walls are of bolted iron plates, and the slate floor is 45ft above beach level. Six tubular legs, each of 12in diameter, with diagonal bracing in the lower panels, incline upwards from a base 24ft 6in wide.

The Low Tower (offshore) is 41ft 6in high with an octagonal lantern room 16ft 6in wide by eight feet high. The floor level is 31ft 6in above the causeway. The base is 23ft wide from which rise four inverted A-frame inclined tubular legs, 12in diameter. Both towers have iron-plate panels connecting the legs for a depth of 12ft below the lantern room, an iron veranda at lantern room floor level and a spiral iron staircase around the tower legs.

Initially the lights were oil lamps with silver-plated parabolic reflectors giving fixed (steady) aspects. In 1878 the high light was fitted with a prismatic lens in place of its reflectors and soon after 1900 both lights were converted to gas, the high light being given a flashing aspect. The end of their active service came in 1917 when the channel into Harwich Harbour was marked with lighted buoys and the Dovercourt lights were finally extinguished. Five years later the Dovercourt light towers were handed over to the Harwich Corporation.

The two towers have survived in this hostile marine environment with little damage although they had received no attention for many years until a local conservation group, the Harwich Society, reconditioned the towers in 1985-8. They are now listed buildings. Structures of this type were at one time more common, but the Dovercourt Leading Lights are now the last remaining pair of iron light towers intact in this country, though the structure of Wyre Light at Fleetwood in Lancashire (HEW 0249/02) remains after being burnt out in 1948 and there is another, disused, six miles off Clacton-on-Sea at Gunfleet. (HEW 0116)

HARWICH

E7. Harwich Lighthouses (TM 261324) have had an interesting history of ownership. They were built as leading lights to guide ships through the channel into the harbour. The first pair was a private commercial venture in 1664 for Admiral Sir William Batten, the Master of Trinity House, who was not ashamed to use his organisation's support in his application to the Crown for permission. The original structures were of wood, and by the time of an engraving of Harwich made in 1712, the Low Light was a candle enclosed in a lantern. The lights passed by marriage to the Rebow family, and in 1812 John Rennie senior was consulted about their value, as the government was considering purchasing them. He noted that it was still a coal brazier and that the windows were blackened by smoke, and recommended its rebuilding, with Argand lights and reflectors. The lights remained, however, with Lt-General Rebow, who had them rebuilt in 1818 to the design of Daniel Alexander, who was also consulting engineer to Trinity House and had already built one on Heligoland. The contractors were John & Henry Lee, a London firm who later undertook other works in Harwich. The opportunity was taken to realign the positions slightly to suit the altered channel to seaward. The cost was £8,547, which was recouped from the dues within a year, and when the government eventually passed an Act in 1836 giving them power to purchase the remaining private lights, they had to pay £31,730 for the two at Harwich.

There are two brick lighthouses, 220 yards apart. The High Lighthouse is alongside West Street and the Low Lighthouse is just above the sea wall at the edge of the beach. The High Lighthouse is a brick tower, a nine-sided polygon in plan, 90ft high. The walls have two skins of gault brickwork with stone bands at the first, third and sixth floors. It is 20ft 6in wide at the base, tapering to 13ft at top. There are seven floors, with the main door at first-floor level, approached by a flight of stone steps with an iron hand-rail. Windows and doors have substantial stone architraves. There is a projecting stone canopy over the third-storey windows, with curious brick arches above the canopy. The original light window at third-storey level is now filled with matching brickwork, but the metal frame is still visible. A three-bay recessed lighthouse window is on the top floor. Because the light was required to shine in one direction only, the 'back' of the lighthouse continues in brickwork up past the lantern level, and is able to support a pagoda-style stone cap with a prominent cornice, crowned by a stone urn; the chimney stack penetrates the cap on the west side. The lantern window has a cast-iron lintel carried by cast-iron mullions.

The Low Lighthouse is a brick tower, a 10-sided polygon in plan, 45ft high with a rendered surface. The tower is 18ft wide at the base tapering to 13ft at the top. The walls are 1ft 10in thick. The lighthouse window on the second storey has been modified for use by harbour pilots. At second-floor level there is an exterior iron veranda, three feet wide, supported on raking struts. The tower has a cap similar to that on the High Lighthouse. Surrounding the tower at ground-floor level is a later addition of an 11ft-wide shelter for promenaders.

Because of changes in the approach to the harbour, discussed in Chapter 3, they have not been used as lighthouses since 1863, when they were replaced by those at Dovercourt **(E6)**. The Low Lighthouse is leased to The Harwich Society and houses the Harwich Maritime Museum, which is open to public visits. (HEW 0115)

E8. Parkeston Quay, Harwich (TM 327238), now renamed Harwich International Port, was an entirely new port facility involving massive land reclamation. It was built for the Great Eastern Railway in 1879-83. Since 1863 the company had been author-ised to run its own shipping services, and had invested in new and larger ships to do so. The facilities on the restricted site at Harwich were inadequate and the Harwich Conservancy Board was unable to agree on how to deal with the problem. As a result, the railway company decided in 1874 to construct a deep-water quay, the first in East Anglia, on a new site. This entailed a massive reclamation to join the then Isle of Ray to the mainland, enclosing 600 acres of land within an earth bank 2½ miles long. More than 600,000 cubic yards of material were moved. The new terminal was built on the northern half of this area, where there was deep water close by, and a new town for the railway workers built to its south. When opened, it was called Parkeston Quay, after Charles Parkes, the chairman of the railway.

The 1,800ft-long quay consisted of timber piles driven into the alluvium, anchored back to nine-foot-diameter concrete cylinders with a timber deck. Seven ships were able to tie up alongside at one time. The railway from Manningtree was converted to double track and diverted in a loop to the north side of the reclaimed area; an east-to-north connection was put in at Manningtree to provide for traffic to the Midlands; and a station-cum-hotel was built for passengers to the continent.

The quay was extended by a further 1,080ft in 1906, designed in reinforced concrete by Louis Mouchel, an early use of that material for marine work. This also enabled further reclamation to take place. It was further extended and rebuilt in 1933-4 when the whole was replaced in reinforced concrete. Roll-on/roll-off berths and the first freightliner terminal in Britain further improved the facilities of the port. It was privatised in 1984. It is still possible to make out something of the original lie of the land, where Ramsey Creek wends its way though undeveloped land between Parkeston and the 'mainland'. (HEW 1664)

E9. Treadmill Crane, Harwich (TM 362325) is a rare survivor. When hostilities against the Dutch brewed up in 1664, Harwich was well situated to serve as a base for the British fleet. The Duke of York (later King James II) visited the naval dockyard in 1666 and gave orders for improvements, including the provision of a house crane similar to one then at Woolwich. In the following year, with the dockyard being expanded under the direction of Samuel Pepys, the crane was erected on the quayside at a cost of £392. It was made of oak throughout.

The crane was operated by two man-powered treadwheels, each 16ft diameter and 3ft 10in wide, four feet apart on a common axle 14in square. At the ends of the axle, iron spigots rotate in cast-iron sockets. The spokes of the wheel decrease from 4½in by 3¾in at the axle to 3½ by 2¾ at the curb, which consists of three inch by three inch segments with scarfed and wedged joints. The walking surface has 1½in planks with

132 *Harwich Treadmill Crane.*

133 *Southend Pier.*

angled fillets to aid foothold. There was no brake on the wheel, a potential hazard to those working it, though a wooden spar could be levered against it to slow it down.

The body of the crane is a house 26ft 3in by 14ft 10in in plan, with 12in by 12in end posts and 12in by 10in intermediates, all tied together with end and side diagonal bracing; the house has tarred weatherboard walls to two-thirds height (originally full height) and the wooden roof has been replaced by clay pantiles. The jib of the crane is mounted on a vertical post, about which it can rotate through 180 degrees, and projects 17ft 10in beyond the house. It is of 12in by 10in timber, strengthened with a kneeler and raking strut. The lifting chain is wound about the treadwheel axle (which therefore gives a 14:1 reduction ratio), from which it passes along the top of the jib and over a pulley.

When the dockyard ceased to be a Naval station in 1713 it became a private yard and both merchantmen and warships were built there. The crane continued to serve the dockyard and was still in use during the First World War. In 1928 the dockyard closed and the crane was given to the town council, who decided to move it to Harwich Green. F. Harold French, the Borough Engineer, supervised the removal in 1930 and the special problem of moving the wheels, which could not be rolled, was overcome by transporting them on a temporary light railway.

Clearly the crane has been repaired over the years. The wheel has a date '1799' on one part, but the jib may well be original. As a double-wheeled crane, it is unique in Britain. It is a scheduled Ancient Monument and is listed Grade II*; it is preserved by the district council. Access to it is prevented by low iron railings but the outside can easily be seen. (HEW 1482)

SOUTHEND-ON-SEA
E10. Southend Pier (TQ 884850) was only the fourth seaside pier to be erected in Britain, after Ryde on the Isle of Wight, Cromer and the Chain Pier at Brighton. Built in 1829-30, it was a timber structure 1,800ft long. It was extended in 1835 and 1846, on

the latter occasion to the design of James Simpson, one of the most influential waterworks engineers of the time in a venture outside his normal practice. It was then over 6,500ft long. In 1887-8 a new pier of iron on cast-iron screw piles was built to the design of Sir James Brunlees, like Simpson a President of the Institution of Civil Engineers but one with a track record of pier building, including Southport, and railway viaducts over Morecambe Bay and the Solway Firth. The contractors were Arrol Brothers, who were engaged at the same time in building the Forth Bridge. A timber extension was added in 1898 with (Sir) John Wolfe Barry as Engineer, and in 1908 an upper deck at the shore end was built by the Borough Engineer. A dog-leg extension at the far end, also by the Borough Engineer, to accommodate larger vessels was opened in 1929; it is called the Prince George Extension. The total length of the pier is now just over 7,000ft.

134 *Thorrington Tidemill.*

Southend Pier, like the other early ones, was simply a landing stage for the transfer of passengers and goods between ship and shore. From the start it had a horse-drawn tramway along its length for goods and passengers' luggage. When the pier was rebuilt in the 1880s the opportunity was taken to provide an electric motor, powered by the pier's own generator. Over the years the line was upgraded, with more and longer trains, but when the pier was closed for refurbishment in the 1980s the traction was changed to the present diesel service.

The pier has been damaged by fire on at least four occasions, in 1959, 1976, 1995 and 2005, and in 1986 a boat sliced through the section between the old and new pier heads. The 2005 damage is being repaired in 2009. (HEW 0079)

THORRINGTON

E11. Thorrington Tidemill (TM 083194) is one of only four tidemills in the country to survive with their machinery. The Domesday survey recorded a number of tidemills in the convoluted estuaries to the north and south of the Naze. Of these only Thorrington and Woodbridge (**S13**) survive, and elsewhere in Britain there are only two other intact tidemills: Carew in Pembrokeshire (HEW 0803) and Eling, Hants (HEW 1400).

135 *Naze Tower, Walton-on-the-Naze.*

The present mill at Thorrington was built in 1831 on the same site as the previous mills and the date is inscribed on a brick in the base of the building near the door. The mill stands at the head of Alresford Creek leading off the Colne estuary and at high tide water was held in the mill pound to the north of an embanked farm track which passes the mill. On the ebb, water could be channelled from the pound to the external, undershot iron wheel. The millhouse has four storeys and is 30ft 6in by 20ft 4in by 40ft high; the white painted weatherboarded walls give it a distinctively East Anglian appearance. It has a double-pitched slated roof. There is a timber lucam on the east side at fourth-storey level. The water wheel is iron-framed, 16ft diameter, six feet wide, with eight spokes and timber paddles. The 12in-diameter iron main shaft drives a 6ft 6in wooden pit wheel within a brick-lined pit inside the mill. The iron wallower and wooden vertical shaft drive three pairs of four-foot-diameter mill stones on the first floor.

One family of millers, the Coopers, worked it throughout the period 1841 to 1912. The mill ceased work in 1926 when the wheel

136 *Walton Pier, Walton-on-the-Naze.*

failed, but was worked for a short time further by a steam engine. The last private owner was Tom Glover, farmer of the nearby land, who used it as a grain store and so did much to preserve the old mill fabric until 1974, when he sold it to Essex county council. Restoration of the waterwheel and sluice in order to bring the mill back into working order began about 1987 and by 1990 the wheel was turning again. The mill pond is sealed off from the tide so that the farmer may use the water for irrigation; it is fed by a small stream. Reed growth has reduced its area significantly, though an idea of its size can be gained by viewing it from the top storey of the mill. The mill machinery and millstones are intact, but at present the wheel has settled slightly out of alignment and the machinery is not worked. The mill is open to the public occasionally.

The tidemill had a companion windmill situated on higher ground a short distance to the east where the car park now is, but this post mill was reduced to splintered wreckage by a gale on Christmas Eve 1869. (HEW 1579)

WALTON-ON-THE-NAZE

E12. Naze Tower (TM 265235) is one of the few remaining structures around the coast built deliberately to serve as a daymark to sailors. It was built by Trinity House in 1720 on the higher land north of the town, sited to line up with Walton Hall, 350 yards further inland, to guide shipping coming in through the Goldmer Gap in the sands. It is an octagonal brick tower, 18ft 6in wide at the base, reducing in two steps to the top. There is an internal staircase with 113 steps, with natural light from round-headed windows only in the two upper stages. Now 86ft high, it was slightly reduced in height during the 19th century, when a reinforcing frame was also inserted at the top. The tower has been used for other purposes at various times, including as a signal post by the Royal Navy, and in the Second World War it supported a radar dish.

It is the largest and highest unlit beacon on the coast of the British Isles and is listed Grade II*. After lying derelict for some time it was taken over and renovated by a local family and is now open during summer months with a museum, art gallery and viewing platform on the top. (HEW 0749)

E13. Walton Pier (TM 254215) was only the fourth seaside pier to be built in Britain, Southend (**E10**) having been started the previous year but also completed in 1830. It was then a timber landing stage 330ft long. It became one of a number of piers on the east coast as far north as Great Yarmouth where steamships brought day trippers from

towns along the Thames. It prospered, but as the coastline altered it became necessary to build a longer pier; this was done in 1869 by Peter Bruff, who had bought land in the neighbourhood in 1855 and built the railway to the town in 1867. The pier was sold in 1897 to the New Walton Pier Company, and they extended it the following year to its present length of 2,600ft; it is now the third longest in the country after Southend and Southport. The shore end of the pier has been widened considerably and there is a large hangar-like amusement arcade covering the structure; some parts of the 1895 structure remain. Beyond it the pier is much as it was a hundred years ago, with concrete piles and crossheads supporting a timber deck. It is popular with sea anglers. The lifeboat station near the seaward end of the pier was opened in 2005. (HEW 1659)

WICKHAM BISHOPS

E14. Wickham Bishops Viaduct (TM 824117) is believed to be the only remaining timber railway viaduct in England, though there is one in Scotland and a few in Wales still in use. It was one of several on the now dismantled Maldon, Witham & Braintree Railway whose Engineer, Joseph Locke, designed it. It was built by Thomas Jackson, one of two successful railway contractors of that name, though his contract for this line was not one of his most rewarding; at its end he was found to have received £376 too much and had to repay it to the company. Nevertheless, his workmanship must have been good and it is remarkable that a timber structure has survived so long, even allowing for the inevitable repairs and replacements over time. When it was opened in 1848 it was about 500ft long, but later the part over land between the two channels of the River Blackwater was replaced by a short embankment. The line over it was reduced to a single track in 1854 and the viaduct itself reduced in width, possibly at that time or in 1860 when substantial repairs were made.

The railway closed in 1966 and the track was lifted in 1969. The viaduct became overgrown and decayed until it was taken over by Essex county council in 1993 and restored by them in 1995. It now has 10 plus 12 spans with piers and deck both formed of 12in by 12in timbers. It has been given Ancient Monument status. A public footpath from Wickham Mill Bridge on the B1018 along the river to Blue Mills Bridge passes under the northern Mill Stream Viaduct. (HEW 1723)

SUTTON BRIDGE

L1. River Nene Outfall is so intimately bound up with the drainage of the Cambridge-shire Fens that it is described here. In the 18th century, navigation up to Wisbech and the drainage of the North and Middle Levels were both badly impeded by the poor state of the river's outfall to the Wash. The situation was improved significantly by the opening of **Kinderley's Cut (N24)** in 1773, but below Gunthorpe Sluice the river ran through unreclaimed marshlands. The channel was shallow and liable to silt up, which caused it to migrate laterally, sometimes by as much as a mile in the course of a year. In 1814 John Rennie senior proposed cutting a new channel through reclaimed land to Crab Hole in the Wash, where there was sufficient depth to allow a constant gradient and so permit the channel to be self-scouring. As so often with proposals of this sort, argument raged about whether it was affordable or even desirable, and if so, whether some other line might not be preferable. Rennie reported again in 1821, rejecting a line through the sands that might be slightly cheaper to cut but would be almost impossible to maintain. Thomas Telford, brought in by Wisbech Corporation, agreed.

There had also been agitation for an embanked road and bridge across the estuary to open a line of communication between Norfolk and the East Midlands, which had become more desirable with the bridging of the Welland at Fosdyke in 1811 and the Great Ouse at King's Lynn in 1823. The Act for the Cross Keys Bridge (later known as Sutton Bridge) was passed in 1826 and for the Nene Outfall in 1827. Under the latter Act, responsibility for building the bridge passed to the Outfall Commissioners, who were required to do so before excavating the channel for the river beneath it. Both projects were designed by (Sir) John Rennie, with Telford as joint Engineer to represent the navigation interests. The contracts for both were awarded to Jolliffe & Banks, who had earlier completed the **Eau Brink Cut (N25)**. The contract was signed on 2 July 1827 and soon more than 1,200 men were at work. The outfall was completed in 1830, with the dam at its lower end being removed on 4 June and the upper three days later. It had

138   *River Nene Outfall.*

been expected that the river would scour out its bed but this did not happen until dams were built across the old bed and the river was confined to the new.

Now, however, the action was so vigorous that it was necessary to protect the banks with stone. Even worse, the piled foundations of the bridge, which had been driven from original ground level as required by the Act, were in great danger of being undermined, and stone was tipped into the river in order to protect them. The resulting shoals reduced the depth seriously and caused eddies that made navigation difficult, problems that were not overcome until a replacement bridge was built in 1850. The present bridge is the third (each on a slightly different site from its predecessor), opened for road and rail traffic in 1897; the railway was removed in 1963.

The embankment from Cross Keys is nearly two miles long; 900 men were employed in its construction and it was opened in July 1831; for about a year coaches had crossed the bridge and descended to the traditional route over the sands. As well as providing a turnpike road, it enabled the reclamation of 1,322 acres of fertile land which provided the Cross Keys Bridge Company with additional income to pay off the capital cost and keep it in repair. The Nene Outfall Amendment Act of 1829 authorised the Outfall Commissioners to erect lighthouses or daymarks at Guy's Head (Guy's Hospital owned much of the land here). The towers, 40ft high, never had lights and today are privately owned; the one on the east bank was the home of Sir Peter Scott for many years. When it was built it was at the end of a long training embankment for the river. Since then other banks have been built, in 1847, 1861, 1867, 1873, 1910 and 1917, which brought the land on the east side up to the tower; further embankments in 1927 and 1956 have taken it considerably further north. (HEW 1274)

L2. North Level Outfall Sluice (TF 467181) is the fourth to be built, each on a different site, since the first was constructed as part of Vermuyden's works under an Act of 1649. The diversion of the River Nene **(L1)** to a new channel and the cutting of the **North Level Main Drain (C32)** required the building of a sluice at the new junction. It was designed by Thomas Pear II and Thomas Telford, with a sill eight feet lower than the old one, which was on the east side of the new river, where a farm is still called Gunthorpe Sluice Farm. Changes caused by better drainage in the Level and the lowering of the Nene's bed led to the North Level Act of 1857, by which the Main Drain was widened and deepened. The outlet was curved slightly to the north of the old and the present sluice was built by Smith & Knight to the design of George Robert Stephenson (1819-1905), cousin and partner of Robert Stephenson. A plaque on the structure records the date 1859. Three openings of 10ft, 20ft and 10ft have rising gates on the upstream face and iron gates on the downstream; the latter close by themselves as the rising tide flows through. The

139 *North Level Outfall Sluice.*

1830 sluice was buried in an embankment but typical Telford cast-iron railings are still visible a short way along the side road to Foul Anchor.

Almost immediately there were problems with seepage under the structure. When the wing walls bulged in 1866, they were taken down, rebuilt and a cast-iron strut placed between to prop them apart; this doubles as a footbridge. This work was done to the design of Benjamin P. Stockman, who had been appointed Engineer to the North Level Commission in 1865 on the resignation of G.R. Stephenson. Later repairs are also recorded on the downstream face of the sluice. (HEW 1764)

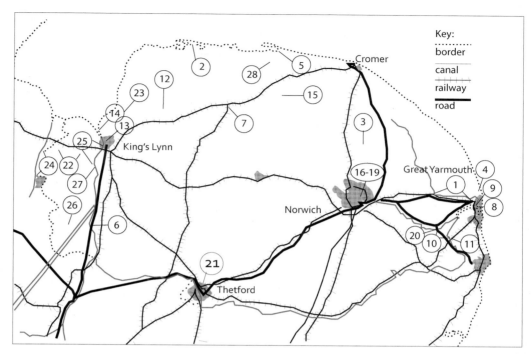

Map of Norfolk.

N1. Acle New Road
N2. Burnham Marshes reclamation
N3. Mayton Bridge
N4. Caister Water Tower
N5. Cley Marshes reclamation
N6. Denver Sluice
N7. Fakenham Gas Works
N8. Town Hall underpinning
N9. Vauxhall Bridge
N10. Haddiscoe Cut
N11. St Olaves Bridge
N12. Houghton Hall water supply
N13. King's Lynn Docks
N14. Norfolk Estuary

N15. Midland & Great Northern Railway
N16. Bishop Bridge
N17. Blackfriars Bridge
N18. Coslany Bridge
N19. St Crispins Bridge
N20. Reedham and Somerleyton Swing Bridge
N21. Town Bridge, Thetford
N22. Old Sea Bank
N23. Appleton Water Tower
N24. Kinderley's Cut
N25. Eau Brink Cut
N26. Middle Level Main Drain
N27. Middle Level Outfall Sluice
N28. Wiveton Bridge

ACLE

N1. Acle New Road (TG 402104 to TG 520081) was an 1830s road constructed on an entirely new alignment. Up to the 1820s, the road from Norwich to Great Yarmouth made a large loop to the north after Acle through Filby (the modern A1064) in order to avoid the low-lying marshy land around the River Bure. About 1826/7 Robert Cory junior, a citizen of Great Yarmouth, promoted a new road from the town to Acle, to be constructed over the marshes south of the River Bure to replace the existing road. It would cut three miles, five furlongs off the distance between the two places. For some reason, whether opposition from landowners or more probably lack of finance, he gave up the idea and contented himself with obtaining an Act of Parliament that allowed him to build a suspension bridge over the Bure, to replace the ferry that he had owned since 1810. A clause in the Act forbade the erection of any other bridge over the river in the neighbourhood. In 1828 surveys were made by two firms of Norwich surveyors, Isaac Lenny and Pratt & Warren; the former planned a very direct route south of the river that would end at Cory's (toll) bridge, the latter would cross the river at Stokesby and keep close to the northern edge of the marshes. Lenny's road was estimated to cost £8,000 and Pratt & Warren's £4,500; although the latter was rather longer than the southern route it would be easier to construct, and would not depend for access to Great Yarmouth on Cory's bridge. In the event the southern route attracted the support of the neighbourhood, although the estimate rose to £9,000 and Lenny had to canvass the local gentry directly to complete the subscription. The necessary Act of Parliament was passed on 3 May 1830. Apart from the usual clauses in a Turnpike Act, it gave the trustees of the Acle New Road the power to hire the tolls of Cory's bridge.

When tenders, on a design-and-build basis, were received on 16 June 1830, it was found that the lowest one exceeded the funds available. The shareholders agreed to increase their subscriptions but a meeting on 28 June decided that a further £1,300 was

140 *Acle New Road, Great Yarmouth to Acle, survey 1828 (Norfolk Record Office – NRO: C/Scf 1/502).*

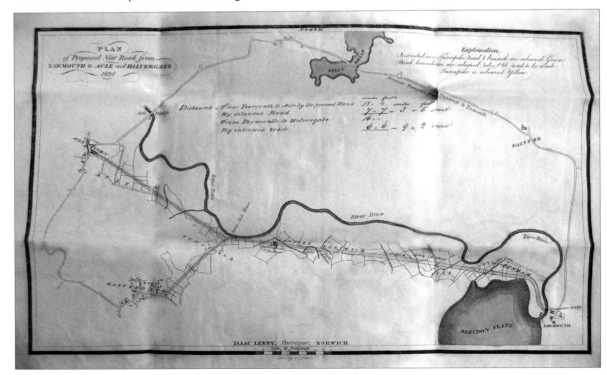

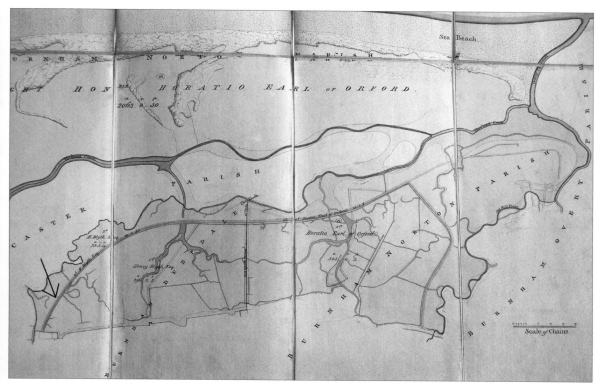

141 Burnham Marshes reclamation award, 1825. The embankment is the triple broad line marked by the arrow (Norfolk Record Office – NRO: BRA 2624/1).

necessary before starting work. This was presumably forthcoming and the contract was awarded to William Thorold, a Norwich civil engineer. The road was opened 'for public inspection' on 13 April 1831 and shortly afterward was used for traffic. Despite this, Thorold and the trustees were still in dispute in July 1832, when the parties were reconciled and Thorold agreed to finish the works.

It is probable that the road was built on a mattress of reed bundles where it crossed the marshes. Now the A47, leaving Runham on the west bank of the Bure, the road goes north-west for about three-quarters of a mile before turning due west and going dead straight ('the Acle Straight') for 4½ miles. At Seven Mile House it bends a little to the north and another straight, of 2¼ miles, takes it to Acle. The branch to Halvergate was also laid out straight. (HEW 2699)

BURNHAM

N2. Burnham Marshes reclamation (TF 835451) was the only land reclamation scheme in England with Thomas Telford as Engineer, though he was also responsible for the Fleet Mound in Sutherland (HEW 0132). A plan for the enclosure and drainage of the salt marshes at Burnham was made by Henry Robinson Palmer, one of the founders of the Institution of Civil Engineers, under the direction of Telford in 1819. The Act for these works together with other enclosures in Burnham Overy was passed on 19 April 1821. The commissioner for the enclosure was John Dugdale of Swaffham. The works were carried out by Thomas Baylis, who had worked for Telford on the Gloucester & Berkeley Canal but had been obliged to give up that contract because of a dispute with the resident engineer about the quality of stone. Telford had written approvingly of Baylis, who despite this problem then went on to work on the Holyhead Road for Telford, and his presence at Burnham can be taken as further approval by Telford.

An embankment about two miles long was constructed over the existing salt marshes, with sluices to allow drainage off the land to the sea. The Act stated that about 390 acres of land in Burnham Norton and 282 acres in Burnham Deepdale would be reclaimed, but the figures given in the plan accompanying the award were 303 and 296 acres respectively, with a further 73 acres in Burnham Deepdale outside the embankment and a large area north and east of the embankment in Burnham Norton. The costs were borne by the landowners, the Earl of Orford and Henry Blyth. The final plan showing the work was made in 1825 and the enclosure award was made on 10 February 1826.

Although some of the land is used for arable, most of it has now been allowed to revert to summer grazing or is designated a nature reserve. (HEW 2701)

BUXTON

N3. Mayton Bridge (TG 250216) is an early brick bridge across the old channel of the River Bure whose history is unknown. Its two arches of 12ft 9in and 9ft span are unusual among brick bridges in being four-centred, which suggests a date from the 15th or 16th century. The bricks are 2in thick and the arch rings are two bricks deep, unnecessary for such a small span and which may indicate some mistrust of the quality of what was then a new material in bridge building. A unique feature is the small shelters built into each end of the upstream parapet. In the 1930s the main channel of the river was still crossed by a timber bridge. (HEW 1542)

142　*Mayton Bridge, Buxton.*

CAISTER-on-SEA

N4. Caister Water Tower (TG 514132) was claimed when it was built in 1932 for the Great Yarmouth Water Works Company to have the largest Intze tank in Britain, with a capacity of 784,000 gallons. It is one of several built on principles developed by Professor Otto Intze of the Technische Hochschule at Aachen, Germany by 1883, with a complicated design of floor to the tank that eliminated changes in stress as the tank filled or emptied. The 570 tons of concrete in the floor at Caister were poured in a single operation, a considerable achievement at that date. It was designed and built by the Trussed Concrete Steel Co. Ltd. It has a double tank – a 79ft-diameter tank on top of a 12-sided shaft of 53ft diameter. It is 123ft from ground level to underside of tank, 161ft 9in to the top. The foundations are piled. (HEW 2686)

143　*Caister Water Tower.*

CLEY

N5. Cley Marshes reclamation (TG 0244/TG 0444) was the subject of discord at various times. Attempts to embank the marshes had taken place by 1522, when John Carleton journeyed from Enfield to Cley to view 'the decay of the haven there through the winning of a marsh at Salthouse by Sir John Heydon, Knight', and the Duke of Rutland's tenants petitioned the Star Chamber against an embankment at Cley. The banks were removed. In the 1630s a Dutchman called Van Hasedunck built a bank at Salthouse, east of Cley, connecting Greneburgh Hill, Great Eye, Little Eye and Flat Eye, which obstructed the channel of the Weybourne and Kelling becks and impounded their water, but a map of 1648 shows the embankment no longer obstructing the channel that led to Salthouse.

A bank with a sluice was built across the mouth of the Glaven (near the site of the present A149 road) for Sir Henry Calthorpe and his son Philip during 1637, possibly under the supervision of Van Hasedunck. This not only shut out the tide but prevented ships sailing up to the quays at Wiveton or Newgate Green. This led to a series of legal actions for its removal, in the Admiral Court at Cley, then when no redress was obtained, in the (manorial) General Court, then to the Privy Council, which was at last successful.

A new straight channel for the river's outfall was dug soon after the passing of the Blakeney Harbour Act of 1 July 1817. The bank across the Glaven was built as part of the Wiveton and Cley Enclosure Act of 1821 based on a scheme proposed by a local man, Benjamin Leak (or Leake), in 1817. He consulted John Rennie senior in 1821 who, unable to spare the time to visit the site but relying on Leak's information, gave his opinion that 'they cannot at the same time improve the harbour by such a scheme but rather accelerate its decay'. In 1822 Thomas Townshend, resident engineer of the Eau Brink works at King's Lynn **(N25)**, was engaged to reconsider the scheme; he estimated £3,300 to complete it. This was unwelcome, so Thomas Telford was consulted:

> In determining upon the plan to be adopted, Mr Telford will please to take into consideration the effect which it will have upon the harbour of Cley, any injury to which must be avoided, and the improvement thereof is an object, so far as it can be effected without any material addition to expense.

He reported,

> from all the experience I have had of tidal rivers connected with drainage and navigation, I am convinced that both these objects are materially concerned in preserving a good outfall; and that this is to be most effectually obtained by suffering a free and full flux and reflux of tidal water as far as possible into the country; and I must add, that all other attempts by means of sluices, have uniformly proved not only ineffectual but prejudicial.

To implement this, Telford proposed to embank the river up to Glandford so that it would be tidal up to that place. This was unacceptable to the landowners who were promoting the enclosure, so they asked John Smith of Holt for a report. He advocated the former scheme, though he recognised that silt would continue to accumulate at Cley and obstruct the harbour, and it was readopted. The bank was complete by 1824.

The marshes are now a bird sanctuary managed by Norfolk Wildlife Trust, who have a visitor centre beside the main road at TG 054441. There is an admission charge there, but access to the marshes and their boardwalks is free. The whole area is part of a designated Heritage Coast. (HEW 1756) (Cley Windmill, HEW 1581)

DENVER
N6. Denver Sluice (TF 587010), together with others in its vicinity, form the Denver Complex, the focal point of all fenland drainage. It is located on the River Ely Ouse at its confluence with the Old and New Bedford Rivers, and prevents the influx of tidal water from the Wash while retaining fresh water in the South Level rivers system. Downstream of the sluice the tidal River Great Ouse flows to (and from) Kings Lynn. The present sluice is the latest in a series that have been built at this location; three

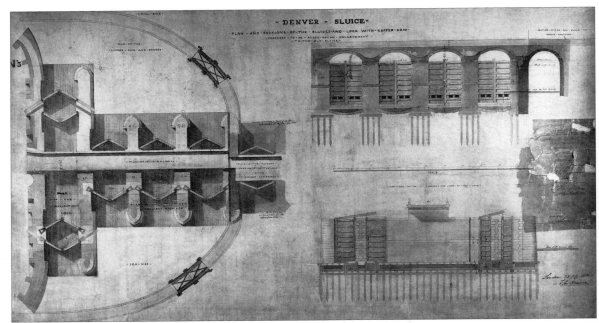

sluiceways and a lock comprise the majority of the present structure, designed by Sir John Rennie. Alongside is the 'Big Eye' sluiceway constructed by the Ouse Drainage Board in 1923.

In the first sasse or navigation sluice was built in 1651-3 under the supervision of Sir Jonas Moore, Surveyor General, as part of Sir Cornelius Vermuyden's campaign of fen drainage. It had two openings giving 24ft of waterway, with one set of doors to keep out the tides and another facing upstream to maintain a level of water for boats navigating to Ely and points beyond. However, experience soon showed that more waterway was needed and in April 1655 Moore let a contract to John Savery for another timber-framed structure to give three openings, each of 10ft; the foundations were probably constructed by direct labour.

In 1682 Ralph Peirson reported that the 1655 structure ought to be rebuilt in brick, with three openings, this time of 12ft, 18ft and 12ft. Work on the foundations began in June but in November Sir Thomas Fitch, the contractor for the Fleet Canal in London, was consulted in November 1682 and it was probably he who suggested that the openings be increased to 18ft each. The sea doors were 18ft high. The foundations were presumably modified to suit and were complete by May 1683. The superstructure was built by contract with the carpenter John Hayward of Southwark, with Sir Thomas's younger brother John as subcontractor for the brickwork and masonry. It was completed in March 1684 for £3,059; the foundations had cost £1,774.

Richard Russell, Peirson's successor as surveyor of the South Level, reported in November 1685 that the eastern sluice of 1653 was also in bad condition. Temporary repairs were put in hand but from May 1699 a completely new structure was built by direct labour. It was completed shortly before Russell's death in July 1700 and cost just over £3,000.

In 1713 the western 1684 structure blew up as a result of a combination of flood waters and tidal surge, though the eastern sluice survived. There had always been opposition to the presence of any sluice at all, and it was not rebuilt at that time. The Ely Ouse effectively became tidal once more and despite the contrarians, the silting at King's Lynn became worse. In 1745 Charles Labelye, the Engineer of Westminster Bridge, was consulted and he advised modifying the eastern sluice and building a new wooden structure on the western site with 20 doors, all to be kept open except in time of flood. His proposals were not adopted, possibly because of the additional embanking that would have been required upstream. Instead proposals by John Leaford, incorporating improved foundations with dovetailed sheet piling, were agreed. This, together with modifications to the eastern structure, were built to Leaford's design and under his supervision in 1746-50.

In 1830 (Sir) John Rennie designed a new structure with three openings of 17ft 6in each and a navigation lock to replace Russell's Eye, as the 1700 structure was known. This would be built immediately to the east of the old, and part of the eastern opening of the old structure would be incorporated in the new. Its sill would be six feet lower than the old. The navigation lock would have pairs of mitre gates pointing upstream and downstream so as to be operable whether the tidal side was higher or lower than the river. Tenders were returned in February 1832 and after some discussions about the terms of the contract, it was signed with James and Joseph Thornton on 20 October 1832. Sir John Rennie inspected the works on 29 August 1835, when only some minor finishing touches were required, and certified that the works were substantially complete and the quality of workmanship excellent. The contractors' final account was £28,994 14s. od.

The three sluices are known as the Little Eyes. In 1923 another, larger, lock was added on the west side to improve the discharge capacity and allow barge traffic to use the river. It is known as the Big Eye. The traffic did not develop as expected and the Big Eye became redundant; it is now permanently sealed off. The upstream mitre gates of the sluices have been replaced by vertically-rising steel gates but the Bramley Fall stone and brick Rennie substructure survives with only minor modification.

The Denver Sluice is now part of the Denver Complex, which was created by the construction in the 1950s/60s of the Cut-off Channel round the east side of the South Level and the Flood Relief Channel that allows some water to bypass the Denver Sluice as well as taking that from the Cut-off Channel. Other structures nearby include a diversion sluice, Relief Channel Lock, Residual Flow Sluice and the Head Sluice or A.G. Wright Sluice. (HEW 0821)

FAKENHAM

N7. Fakenham Gas Works (TF 919293) is the only remaining complete gas works in England, though there is also one in Scotland at Biggar. There is no record remaining of the early days of the works. The present works were opened in 1846, when the *Norwich Mercury* reported on 21 November that Fakenham had just been lit by gas, through the exertions of R.P. Spice 'whose engagements as a gas engineer are of an extensive

145 *Fakenham Gas Works, gasholder.*

character'. It was a private company of shareholders, as was usual at that time. *White's Guide to Norfolk* reported in 1854 that the gasholder would hold 4,900 cubic feet of gas, and in 1864 that the works had been enlarged in 1856. One oral tradition suggests that the first retort house was near the road. A circular area to the west of the valve house appears to have been the site of the first gasholder.

Existing buildings include: horizontal retorts dating from 1907 and 1910; purifiers by Newton Chambers, 1906; Livesey washer, 1920 and condensers, 1953, by Firth Blakeley of Church Fenton, Yorkshire; station meter by Gas Meter Company, 1929. The remaining gas holder consists of cast-iron panels and is dated 1888 – it holds 14,000 cu.ft.

The works ceased production in September 1965 when feeder mains were completed to bring gas in from the Eastern Gas Board's main transmission system. They were then converted into a museum, and reopened in 1987. The museum is run by a small body of local volunteers. It is open at limited times on Thursdays, and on some other days in summer. Details are available on the trust's website, www.fakenhamgasmuseum. com. (HEW 0096)

GREAT YARMOUTH

N8. Town Hall underpinning (TG 522074) used innovative techniques to save time and money. The new Town Hall at Great Yarmouth had been built in 1878-82, partly on the site of and partly overlapping the old. It was 132ft by 108ft by 50ft high to the parapet, with a clock tower 110ft high. Its weight was about 5,000 tons. The subsoil consisted of a gravel bank, underlying 16 to 18ft of ooze and five to six feet of made ground, into which trenches were cut for the concrete foundations. The wooden quay front of the River Yare was 70ft west of the west front of the new building.

The structure soon showed signs of unequal subsidence, which continued until early in 1886 it approached the limit of safety, and an attempt was made to underpin the worst part by inserting concrete blocks beneath the foundation, but it proved impossible to remove the groundwater from the excavations without further jeopardising the structure. Another proposal, to insert wrought-iron joists through the brickwork, supported by concrete blocks near the surface of the ground, was also rejected. By November 1886 the west front was found to have sunk 12½in more than the east side, there were cracks in the brickwork and the building was leaning towards the river. The town council decided to demolish the western section and rebuild on more solid foundations.

Instead, a scheme was submitted by F.E. Duckham and J.E. Teasdel by which this portion could be supported and raised back to the level of least settlement, and would include the straightening and repair of the walls. It was estimated to cost about half the cost or rebuilding and to take only one third of the time. To start, the walls were shored by heavy-duty props. Then hollow cast-iron piles, outside the original concrete

146 *Great Yarmouth Town Hall.*

147 *Vauxhall Bridge, Great Yarmouth.* foundations, were screwed into the gravel, cleared of earth and filled with concrete. Since it was thought that the cast iron might be corroded by the soil, the concrete core was designed to be large enough to carry the weight without the benefit of the iron. Double lines of rolled girders were placed, parallel to the building's walls, on top of the piles. Wrought-iron joists were passed under the foundations from one line of girders to the other and suspended from the girders by means of long, threaded bolts.

The tower, being heavier, was supported on caissons, sited asymmetrically along the north and south faces to suit the existing walls. Platforms of joists on top of these supported four lines of lattice girders, from which were suspended joists passing right through from east to west.

By sequential and progressive tightening of the bolts, the load from the building was transferred to the piles and caissons and then the lower parts of the building were raised to the desired level. When all had been achieved, the ground around was cleared to a depth of two feet and these trenches filled with concrete so as to encase the tops of the piles and all of the suspended ironwork. The damaged brickwork was cut out and replaced and any consequential interior work made good.

The work started in May 1887 and was completed within 12 months. The original building cost £30,000 and the cost was of the remedial works was well within the £8,250 estimate. (HEW 2695)

N9. Vauxhall Bridge (TG 521080) is a unique example of bridge modification. It links the original railway station in Great Yarmouth, Vauxhall Station, to the town. When the station was built, on the far side of the River Bure from the town, the only access to it from the town was across the Suspension Bridge, which had been erected in 1828-9 and enjoyed a statutory monopoly of crossing the river in the town. The Suspension Bridge collapsed in 1845, leaving the only access to the station by the ferry which the bridge owner now laid on. The Suspension Bridge was replaced by a wrought iron bowstring girder, but the Norfolk Railway obtained an Act to abolish the monopoly and erect a bridge of their own, which as well as a road would carry a freight-only tramway to the South Quays on the town side. Probably because of lack of money, Vauxhall Bridge was not fully opened until 1852. It was a single 115ft span, with two wrought-iron

Fairbairn-type box girders 1ft 10in wide by eight feet deep at 24ft 6in centres. When the Great Eastern Railway, successor to the Norfolk, wished in 1886 to upgrade the line to full railway loading, it added trussed arches above the existing bridge, with iron rod hangers to carry the girders, thus converting the structure to a bowstring girder. This is a unique example of this mode in Britain.

The railway and road have been closed and fenced off and the bridge is now used only by foot-passengers on the walkway attached to the south side of the bridge. The bridge is listed, but is in need of some maintenance if it is to survive in the longer term. (HEW 0391)

HADDISCOE

N10. Haddiscoe New Cut (TG 427014 to TM 456988) is the most visible reminder of the 1820s scheme to make Norwich a port independent of Great Yarmouth. The River Yare and its tributary the River Wensum were navigable from Norwich to the sea below Great Yarmouth in medieval times. Four miles above Yarmouth the river widened out into Breydon Water, a wide expanse at high tide but largely mud flats at low tide. The ebb of the tidal water from this stretch through the narrow exit to the sea helped to scour the exit and, with the aid of training walls, keep it open. But the shallow depth of Breydon Water at its upper end meant that larger vessels could not travel up to Norwich and goods bound to and from the city had to be transhipped at Yarmouth, to the benefit of that town and the disadvantage of the former. Yarmouth also had rights to certain duties on all imports of coal, which added to their cost at Norwich.

In 1814 (Sir) William Cubitt, then working with Ransome's at Ipswich, was asked to report on how best to provide eight feet of water up to Norwich. Because dredging a channel, probably the cheapest way in the short term, would not give a permanent solution, and an embanked channel through Breydon would severely diminish the back water for scour, his proposal was to make a new cut along the south side of Breydon Water and an embankment at its west end to confine the river waters there. The matter lapsed until it was revived in 1818. John Rennie senior, a leading civil engineer of the day who had been consulted on similar schemes elsewhere, was asked by the borough of Great Yarmouth to comment. Although generally in favour, he made a couple of objections, the result of which was that Cubitt was asked to investigate an alternative route to the sea at Lowestoft.

Cubitt made his report on 17 July 1820. The main features were a straight 2½-mile cut between Reedham on the River Yare, a lock at Mutford Bridge in the narrows between

148 *Haddiscoe New Cut.*

Oulton Broad and Lake Lothing, and a cut with a lock between Lake Lothing and the sea at Lowestoft. The lock at Mutford Bridge would have gates pointing both ways so that the fresh water on one side and saltwater on the other would not pass through. The lock at Lowestoft could be used to pen in the water at high tide and release it at low water in order to scour out the harbour. A considerable part of Cubitt's report was devoted to the effects of the new harbour on the coastal regime, where littoral drift was known to occur. The estimated cost was £87,000.

The Norwich interests took a couple of years to deliberate the report and decide to raise the necessary finance, and 1823 was taken up in a war of words between the Norwich committee and the supporters of Yarmouth. In early 1825, however, a time of intense financial speculation, a large subscription was raised in London and these promoters formed a provisional committee of the Norwich & Lowestoft Navigation Company on 15 February. By 11 March £76,500 had been raised. The bill for the project was considered in Parliament in 1826, when evidence was given that the scour of the harbour would be much less than expected and the cost much greater; the bill was rejected. Engineering and Parliamentary expenses to date amounted to £9,100.

In 1827 renewed application was made to Parliament. More emphasis was placed on the benefits to towns on the River Waveney such as Beccles and Bungay, and also in the possibilities of Lowestoft as a harbour of refuge. Cubitt's scheme had been modified by the inclusion of piers to protect the sea entrance, though his estimate had not increased, and the opponents had the benefits of evidence from Hugh McIntosh, the foremost contractor of the day, that he would not do the work for less than £159,427. Despite this, the bill passed into law on 28 May 1827. The costs to date had risen to £14,753.

At the first meeting of the company, Cubitt was appointed Engineer. As had been agreed in Parliament, the first works to proceed would be the lock and embankment at Mutford Bridge, in order to protect the marshlands upstream from any possible incursion of the sea. Work started on 4 September 1827 with Green of Newport as contractor, and the lock was opened in November 1828. Next, the main road at Lowestoft was diverted and the sea lock constructed. It was 150ft long by 50ft wide, and had brickwork 12ft thick. The swing bridge over it was built by John Seaward & Co. of Canal Ironworks, Poplar; they had already built one at St Katharine's Dock in London and the one at Lowestoft was based on it. After successful trials of the sluicing mechanism, the lock was used on 4 June 1831 and formally opened on 10 August.

About this time, Cubitt left the works and George Edwards, who had made some of the original surveys and assisted Cubitt since construction started, was appointed resident engineer. Work had been in progress meanwhile on widening and deepening Oulton Dyke but the capital had been spent without any work being done on the cut from Reedham to Haddiscoe. The company applied to the Exchequer Loan Commissioners for a loan of £50,000 (the maximum permissible) and after reports from Thomas Telford, the commissioners' Engineer (one in answer to objections from the Mayor of Great Yarmouth), the loan was agreed in February 1832. The contract for the cut between the Rivers Yare and Waveney, the Haddiscoe New Cut, was awarded to Thomas Townshend, who was then working on the Birmingham Canal's new main line at Smethwick. It was completed in January 1833, and the first sea-borne cargo arrived at Norwich at the end of the following month. The bridge over the cut at St Olaves was still being erected in July, and the formal opening of the navigation took place on 30 September.

The following years were marred by engineering and the consequential financial troubles. The company was unable to repay even the interest on the loan from the Exchequer Loan Commission. After fruitless efforts to persuade the company to raise the money required for necessary repairs and maintenance, the Commission took possession of the works on 13 December 1834. Wrangles between the company's directors and the Commission continued while the condition of the works, and the income from them, continued to deteriorate, until they were put up for auction in January 1840. An offer of £14,500, for works that had cost more than ten times that sum, was rejected. The commissioners obtained an Act in April 1842 allowing them to close works they owned and to sell the materials, and on this basis they issued a warrant to do so in the case of Lowestoft. This brought forward an offer of £5,000 from Alderman Farncombe of Lowestoft which, in the absence of any higher offers, was accepted. Ownership passed to Farncombe's associates on 10 November 1842. They spent £2,000 in repairs, particularly to the south pier, and sold on the undertaking for £12,500 to (Sir) Samuel Morton Peto in October 1844. (See also **Lowestoft Harbour (S7).**)

N11. St Olaves Bridge (TM 457994) is one of two cast-iron bowstring arch bridges in the country. Its 80ft clear span carries the Great Yarmouth-Bungay road over the River Waveney. In the reign of Edward I a ferry conveyed passengers over the river, but in 1296 the king sent a writ to the Sheriff of Norfolk and Suffolk to build a bridge. A rebuilding was sanctioned in 1422, though it is not clear if much was achieved, and a three-arch bridge built c.1500 was the subject of a painting in Loddon Church.

According to a report presented to Norwich and Beccles Sessions in 1758, the river was 120ft wide here, but the bridge's three ribbed arches spanned only 17, 20 and 18ft so that there was only a passage of 55ft for twice that width of water. It was believed that all the piles that supported the bridge had become exposed and were decayed and hollow. A proposal by the builders of the bridge at Wisbech for a single arch of 55ft span, which would have improved the flow by removing the impediments caused by the piers, was turned down, and one of 60ft requested, but the estimate was rejected as being too expensive. A report in 1761 by William Etheridge, who had built a 150ft timber span at Walton-on-Thames (and also the **Mathematical Bridge (C6)** at Cambridge) also led to no action. Eventually some work was done in 1768, and it remained in much the same inconvenient state until the present bridge was built in 1847-8.

The Engineer for the new bridge was George Edwards of Carlton Colville and the contractors were Henry and Martin Grissell of the Regent's Canal Ironworks, London; the contract price was £5,984. The foundations consist of timber piles and grillages, on which are built the brick abutments. The main arches rise 14ft 6in and are formed of two half-ribs, each 45ft long, bolted together at the centre of the bridge; of 2ft 3in by 2ft 6in

149 *St Olaves Bridge, Haddiscoe.*

section at the centre, they have lattice webs. At 24ft centres across the bridge, they give a 20ft road width. The main ribs are tied at road level by flat-link wrought-iron chains. The ironwork is of good quality and very attractively detailed. Originally the bridge had cast-iron cross-girders and deck suspended by wrought-iron hangers at five-foot centres along the bridge. During the Second World War there was considerable debate about the cost of strengthening in order to remove the weight limit of five tons on the bridge, but nothing was done until 1959-60, when the hangers were replaced in high-tensile steel and the deck in mild steel. The bridge can be inspected at close quarters from the later footbridge on the southern side.

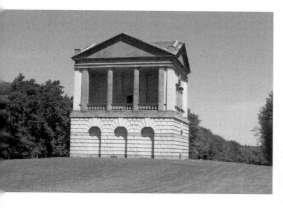

150 *Houghton Hall Water House.*

One factor that argued against a strengthening in 1940 was a weight limit of four tons on the twin-leaf bascule bridge over the New Cut, a short way south of St Olaves. It, too, would have needed to be upgraded, thus adding to the overall cost. Eventually it was bypassed by the Haddiscoe High-Level Bridge, built for £98,000 in 1960-1, and the cast-iron leaves removed. (HEW 0192)

HOUGHTON

N12. Houghton Hall water supply (TF 790295) includes probably the oldest purpose-built water tower in the country. The private water supply to Houghton Hall consists of wells, a pump house and a 'water house', with 1,500 yards of three-inch lead supply pipe servicing the Hall. The system was devised by Sir Robert Walpole, first Prime Minister of England and owner of the estate, and was in operation from about 1732. It may also be the oldest such system with most of its components still extant. Pumping against a static head of about 80ft represented a considerable technological achievement for the time.

The pump house, a single-storey brick building (1728), contains two wells and the pumps. The wells, 67ft deep, are formed by a vertical succession of brick lined bell-shaped chambers accessed via a cast-iron spiral staircase in a separate adjacent shaft. The wells and stair shafts are linked by cross-passages at each level and the crown of each well chamber has a masonry-lined aperture for the pump rods.

The original pump was powered by a horse-gin located in the pump house courtyard. The horse-gin has gone but the overhead wooden shaft connecting the gin to the crankshaft of the three-throw three-cylinder pump in the southern well is still in place. The forged iron crankshaft and pump rods are clearly very old and may be original although this cannot be determined for certain. In 1904 the horse-powered pump was superseded by a Hayward Tyler three-throw three-cylinder pump in the northern well, initially powered by a hot-air engine and later re-engined with a Ruston & Hornsby single-cylinder oil engine.

Water was pumped to the Water House (c.1732) 500 yards from the Pump House for storage and a gravity supply to the Hall. Its two-storey exterior was designed by Lord Herbert in neo-Palladian style. Built in sandstone, brick and stucco on a slight mound, it stands 34ft high and 32ft square with a colonnaded gallery at first-floor level. It is maintained in its original condition and is listed Grade I. The interior contains a 20,000-gallon Braithwaite tank which replaced the original 12,000-gallon tank during the Second World War.

Lord Herbert is known to have been a friend of the noted hydraulic engineer J.T. Desaguliers and it is probable that Desaguliers was involved with the supply around the mid-18th century. (HEW 2172)

KING'S LYNN

N13. King's Lynn Docks (TF 614205) are the only wet docks in East Anglia other than Ipswich. The King's Lynn Dock & Railway Company was formed in 1865. (Sir) James Brunlees and (Sir) George B. Bruce were appointed Engineers on 17 December 1865. Their plans were subjected to review by James Abernethy, whose modifications were accepted. All three were Presidents of the Institution of Civil Engineers at some stage in their careers. Tenders were received from William Ritson, William Eckersley and William Laurence; the latter, although not the lowest, was accepted. Work started on the first dock at the end of July 1866, though the ceremony of laying the first stone did not take place until 9 March 1868. Laurence was also a contractor for railway works and, like many others, suffered financially during the banking crisis of 1866. At one stage the directors of the dock company considered terminating his contract because of his 'pecuniary embarrassments', but the problems were overcome and he completed the work. His tender had been for £81,750 and by the end of June 1869 £81,200 had been spent. The dock was formally opened on 7 July 1869 by the Prince and Princess of Wales, when it was named the Alexandra Dock. It was now the turn of the dock company to be embarrassed. Laurence submitted claims for £5,277 for additional work but the Engineer,

151 *King's Lynn docks.*

Brunlees, only awarded £2,905. Laurence accepted, on certain conditions, presumably in the belief that there was no more money to be had. Shortly afterwards he contracted for some railway lines to improve access to the docks; it is to be hoped that his rates were sufficiently generous to recoup some of his loss.

The Alexandra Dock was sufficiently successful that the directors of the dock company decided to build a second wet dock leading off the existing one. It was designed by John Valentine, who had earlier been the Engineer of a group of railways centred on King's Lynn but was now a consulting engineer in London. The contract for its construction was awarded to Pearson & Son of Bradford, and the final stone was laid on 18 October 1883 by the Duke of Portland, the head of the Bentinck family, after whom the dock was named. Valentine sued the dock company for some professional fees he claimed he was owed; the company counterclaimed because they asserted that the contractor had paid him for some of his work. The Official Referee settled the case by awarding some points to both sides, but relationships cannot have been too badly affected as both Valentine and Weetman Pearson, the head of the contracting firm and later Viscount Cowdray, subsequently became directors of the dock company.

Both docks are still in use. The twin wrought-iron swing bridges constructed by the Cleveland Bridge & Engineering Company over the passage between the two docks are still operational, having been refurbished in 2007.

N14. Norfolk Estuary (TF 52/62) was a very ambitious scheme to reclaim large tracts of land from the Wash. Because of restrictions placed upon it during the parliamentary process, it was much less successful than its promoters had hoped. The suggestion was put forward at a meeting held at the British Coffee House in London on 28 April 1837. Lord William Cavendish Bentinck, MP, a prominent and active landowner in the area, was in the chair, and a report was commissioned from Sir John Rennie, who had been the Engineer for the **River Nene Outfall (L1)** in 1827-30. He surveyed the River Ouse from Hermitage Sluice to Thief Bank in March 1838 and his report was presented to a meeting at the *British Hotel*, Cockspur Street, London on 1 July 1839. Lord William having died two weeks previously, the chair was taken by his nephew, Lord George Bentinck, MP. Rennie proposed to reclaim 158,000 acres of land from the sea, which he considered would be worth £40 per acre; he estimated it would cost £12 per acre to reclaim. He also considered that a further 200,000 acres of existing land could be improved as a consequence of the proposed inning. A survey by Charles Burcham and William Plews, previously associated with Rennie elsewhere, was less visionary, suggesting that 24,000 acres might be reclaimed in six years. A Company of Proprietors of the Great Level of the Wash was formed, to have a capital of 20,000 shares of £100 each. Sir John Rennie and George Rennie were named as the Engineers.

Support for the scheme was canvassed locally and nationally, including a memorial to Sir Robert Peel in December 1842, in which it was stated that the reclaimed area would be called 'Victoria County'; the Crown proposed to take one 20th of land reclaimed in compensation for ceding their rights. A new report by Sir John Rennie on 17 March 1846 was considered by (Sir) William Cubitt and James Rendel, whose own report on 27 April was more guarded:

> Finally we have to assure the Directors that if this report is less conclusive than they might have expected and desired, it is solely to be attributed to our anxiety to avoid raising expectations of success which may not be realized; and, on the other hand, not to discourage the Company from carrying into effect a plan of which their Engineer entertains sanguine expectations, and which we feel cannot be otherwise than one of great public utility, even though it should prove commercially unsuccessful.

Despite this, the directors convinced themselves that they could pay interest on the money advanced while the works were under way and would be able to pay dividends from 1860. The company gained its Act in 1846, but at the expense of severe concessions to powerful vested interests. It was forbidden to embank any lands for reclamation until it had created new cuts through two large sandbanks in the Wash, in order to maintain (and as events turned out, improve) navigation to the port of King's Lynn and to maintain the outflow of the River Ouse necessary for the drainage of the Middle and South Levels.

152 *Norfolk Estuary (Minutes of Proceedings of the Institution of Civil Engineers, vol. 46, 1875-6).*

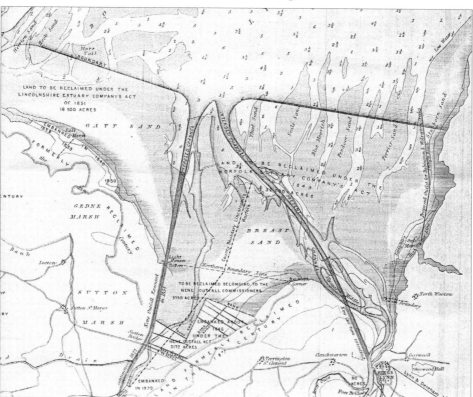

Potential opposition from three owners whose lands fronted the Wash were bought off by being given rights to some of the land to be reclaimed, and George W.P. Bentinck, whose land would be transferred from west of the river to its east, would have his land protected for £1,140 – the cost to the company in the event was about ten times that amount. The number of shares was reduced to 10,000 and their value £50 each, so that the capital was only one quarter of what had been intended by Rennie.

Faced with the need to spend very large sums of money before there was any prospect of an income, the company entered discussions with the corporation of King's Lynn and the Eau Brink Commissioners to obtain financial contributions in return for the benefits they would receive. Each agreed to pay £60,000 and on this basis a revised Act was obtained in 1849, also extending the time limits for the works to be completed.

Following the collapse of the railway mania there had been a shortage of capital available to invest and of the 9,114 shares subscribed for, no less than 2,667 were doubtful. The company tried to bolster public confidence by appointing Robert Stephenson joint Engineer with Rennie, but financial uncertainty meant that it was not until 29 August 1850 that a contract was entered into with Peto & Betts, the well-known contractors, to excavate the two navigation cuts for £143,000. A ceremonial start to the work was made on 8 November.

The contractors made good progress and by the middle of 1852 the Engineers were ready to dam the old channel and turn the waters into the new, in order to use the ebb and flow to scour it out to the depth required by the company's Act. At this stage, the Eau Brink Commissioners asserted that they had made their financial contribution on the basis that the excavation would be to the full depth before the diversion, and obtained an order from the Vice-Chancellor to stop up the works. This order was upheld on appeal to the courts so the company promoted a further Act of Parliament to allow them to carry out the works in the way their Engineers had intended; it was passed on 9 May 1853. Thus, after a year's delay, work resumed the following month, and although the temporary dams needed to be dredged away, the channel otherwise scoured itself satisfactorily.

Work could now commence on embankments and jetties to aid the warping of the marshes. By 1857 the contract with Peto & Betts was effectively cost-plus, as they had reached the quantities of material and stone that they were required to find at their own expense and risk. Accordingly, the contract was ended in February 1858 by mutual negotiation, the company paying them for the work they had done and their out-of-pocket expenses of £2,556 caused by the stoppages of the work. Henceforth a series of contracts was let to W. Sissons of Hull for the different parts of the reclamation. An Act of 1857 allowed the corporation of King's Lynn and the Eau Brink Commissioners to reduce their contributions to £55,000 and further Acts to adjust the company's affairs were passed in 1877 and 1899.

The Norfolk Estuary Company continued to exist until 1964 when, because it had been set up by an Act of Parliament, another Act was necessary to wind it up. It was stated then that some 4,600 acres of land had been reclaimed – a long way short even of the revised proposals which formed the basis of the company's incorporation. (HEW 2702)

MELTON CONSTABLE

N15. Midland & Great Northern Joint Railway (SK 988182 to TG 528079) was an interloper in an area dominated by the Great Eastern Railway. It stretched 112 miles from Little Bytham in Lincolnshire to Great Yarmouth, with branches to Peterborough, Norwich and Cromer. Of its total route mileage of 182½ miles, 109 miles were single line. It

was formed by successive amalgamations of no fewer than 10 small railways. The Act for the first of these, the Norwich & Spalding Railway, was passed in 1853 (it never got nearer to Norwich than Sutton Bridge); the connection to the Midland Railway at Little Bytham was made in 1894. The individual companies were promoted locally, though there is some evidence that in the later stages there was a recognition that a more direct through-route could be established from north Norfolk to the Midlands and the North than that of the other local company, the Great Eastern Railway.

One unusual feature of the line was that its line ran over a swing bridge that had been designed for road traffic, originally called Cross Keys Bridge, now Sutton

153 Melton Constable Water Tower, built by the Midland & Great Northern Joint Railway for its works and the town.

Bridge. The present bridge was designed by J. Allen McDonald of the Midland Railway and erected by Handyside of Derby. The other major bridge on the line was the Breydon Viaduct at Great Yarmouth. Its swing span was 170ft long and, perhaps to even things out, was designed by Alexander Ross of the Great Northern Railway. A type of bridge unique to the Norwich branch was the 'A-frame', two examples of the three that were built having now been incorporated into public footpaths.

The line operated largely independently of its parents and had its own works at Melton Constable, where the branches to Norwich and Cromer left the main line. The present 'railway town' is probably the only one in the country to have been created by so small a line. It was fortunate in having William Marriott as its Engineer, a resourceful and inventive man whose innovative reinforced concrete structures can still be found. The line was closed, with the exception of a few short sections, in 1959, before Beeching but the longest single railway closure of them all. (HEW 1665)

NORWICH
N16. Bishop Bridge (TG 240090) is the only remaining medieval bridge over the River Wensum in Norwich and the most historically important. It has three arches carrying Bishopgate over the River Wensum. In 1275, Edward I granted a patent to the Prior of Norwich, William de Kerkeby, to build a gate with a bridge across the river, replacing an earlier timber bridge. In the late 13th century a distinguished citizen of Norwich,

154 Hellesden railway bridge.

Richard Spynk, built the stone and brick bridge with segmental arches strengthened with stone ribs infilled with brickwork. The gate known as the Ethelbert Gate was built at the west end of the bridge with a fortified gatehouse extending onto the bridge over two of the arches. The bridge and gate were in the ownership of the priory until 1393 when the city formally took possession and rough stone tablets in the parapets display the city arms. An examination of the structure in 1790 revealed serious weaknesses caused by the weight of the gate tower and this was demolished. The roadway over the bridge is wide enough only for single-file traffic with footpaths on both sides but the carriageway may have been wider in earlier days and there are interesting refuges in the parapets, probably for pedestrians.

There are stone ribs in the arches with brick infilling. The spandrels and parapets are built in a mixture of stone and brick-work. Overall length between abutments is 70ft. Spans vary from 15ft to about 25ft. The piers are of stone, with pointed cutwaters at both ends. Width between parapets is 14ft 6in; tarmac-surfaced roadway 10ft 6in wide. There are semi-circular pedestrian refuges in the parapets. (HEW 1776)

N17. Blackfriars Bridge (TG 231088) has an elegant masonry segmental arch of 44ft 6in span and 10ft 4in rise, designed by Sir John Soane. It was constructed in 1783-4 by a local builder, John de Carle, using Portland stone ashlar. The stone vous-soirs stand slightly proud of the spandrels and have chamfered edges so that each is visually separate from its neighbour. In fact the workmanship of the arch was of a high order. The specification called for the edge of each voussoir to be perfectly smooth and to be set in dry milled lead. Adjacent voussoirs are additionally connected by two iron tubes let into them equally and run in with lead. The ornate railings are of cast iron. The width of 19ft 9in between them allowed only for a 10ft carriageway plus footpaths, but the bridge has now been given over entirely to pedestrians. (HEW 1123)

N18. Coslany Bridge (TG 227088) is, with **Culford Hall Bridge (S3)**, the oldest remaining cast-iron bridge in the region. Each of its four ribs, of five sections bolted together, spans 36ft. The spandrels and parapets are solid. The central panel on the outer face of both parapets carries a plaque bearing the city arms and the centre of the arch is cast-marked '1804'. A spout for hoses projects from the west parapet.

The bridge was designed by James Frost jr, a carpenter of St Faith's Lane, Norwich, with modifications suggested by William Jessop, and built by Frost under a contract worth £1,100. The bridge has survived the tests of nearly two centuries, including the flood in 1912 which reached parapet level. It has been tastefully restored (apart from the discordant feature of the modern tubular handrails) and the complete width of 15ft between the parapets has been paved in brick. (HEW 1125)

N19. St Crispins Bridge (TG 226092) is a late 19th-century wrought-iron bridge by a local contractor. Formerly called Station Bridge, it was built to provide access to the City Station of the Eastern & Midlands Railway (later the **Midland & Great Northern Joint (N15)**), the terminus of a line opened in 1882. It is a wrought-iron arch of 55ft span and five-foot rise, with latticed spandrels. The legend 'Norwich Barnard, Bishop, & Barnards. 1882' is prominently displayed on the fascia. The arch is made up from pieces of plate and angle iron riveted together as was usual at the time, and the parapets are good examples of cast iron. After the station closed, the bridge

155   *Bishop Bridge, Norwich.*

156   *Blackfriars Bridge, Norwich.*

157   *Coslany Bridge, Norwich.*

became part of the ring road, with a modern bridge alongside for the other half of a dual carriageway. (HEW 1124)

REEDHAM, SOMERLEYTON

N20. Reedham and Somerleyton Swing Bridges (TG 422017 and TM 476967) are large but light swing bridges for railway traffic. They are on the sites of structures built for the Lowestoft Railway & Harbour Co. to the design of George Bidder. Those were centrally-pivotted, cast-iron structures of the type seen also at Norwich Trowse and Oulton Broad **(S8)** with timber approach spans. The line was opened on 3 May 1847.

The bridges were rebuilt for double track in 1904-5. Each swing section rotates on 16in-diameter cast-steel wheels and a 10in-diameter central pivot carried on a central brick pier of 27ft 6in diameter. The superstructure is a wrought-iron truss, 19ft deep at the centre and seven feet at the ends. Heavy plate girders 139ft long as the bottom chord take the live load from the rail traffic, and the lighter upper members carry the cantilevered ends when open to river traffic. Somerleyton carries the railway over the River Waveney and gives a clear opening of 55ft. It is swung regularly in summer for holiday traffic but rarely in winter.

The original Act for the railway specified a clear opening of 55ft, but at Reedham the company simply ignored its obligation and provided only 50ft, despite legal action from Norwich Corporation's River Committee. Presumably the contractors, Grissell & Peto, wished to use the same design that they had provided at Trowse. When Reedham was rebuilt, on a new line 28ft 6in upstream from the old, the opportunity was taken to place the central pier near the south bank instead of the north, enabling the full 55ft width to be provided. There is a minimum 11ft headway when the bridge is across the river, but from time to time it is damaged by coastal ships going to and from Norwich. This can upset the weight distribution between the two halves, causing bearing problems.

159 *Reedham Bridge, open to river traffic.*

Originally operated by a Crossley oil engine, it is now done by electric and hydraulic power. (HEWs 0745 and 0746)

THETFORD

N21. Town Bridge, Thetford (TL 868831) has a nicely proportioned cast-iron arch of semi-elliptical shape with a span of 33ft across the Little Ouse River. There are six ribs, each 15½in deep, with a bottom flange five inches by 1½in but no top flange. Bedplates resting on the bottom flange carry fill on which the road is formed; this form of construction harks back to **Coslany Bridge (N18)** 25 years

earlier. The outer ribs carry solid spandrels decorated with circles; the south-east face of the arch bears the date of building, 1829, and the other side carries the emblem of a castle. The cast-iron parapet fences are made in an intricate pattern and at the centres there are ornate lamp posts. Town Bridge was designed by Francis Stone, the county surveyor, and built by Bough & Smith, a firm of civil engineering contractors based in London. The same designer and contractors were responsible in 1828-9 for the similar cast-iron Fye Bridge in Norwich; it was replaced in 1933.

160 *Town Bridge, Thetford.*

The road over the bridge narrows to 15ft, with a marked hump, and as traffic levels grew on the A11 London to Norwich road the restrictive width hastened the construction of an alternative main route through the town. This diversion of heavy traffic and the discreet strengthening of the deck with reinforced concrete arches between the cast-iron ribs, carried out by the county council in 1964, has greatly extended the life of this Grade-II listed structure. The town council has made the river bank area into a distinctive feature incorporating the bridge. (HEW 1641)

WALPOLE ST ANDREW

N22. Old Sea Bank is a large-scale sea defence work that almost certainly dates in part from Saxon times. The north-west and south-west shores of the Wash are bounded, some distance inland, by a low earth bank following a sinuous 80-mile route from Skegness to King's Lynn. This is clearly shown in many places on the local OS 1:50,000 and 1:25,000 scale maps as 'Sea Bank' in antique-style lettering, and it stands out on the map in marked contrast to the straight lines of the more modern fenland landscape features.

The length of the Sea Bank as given above can only be regarded as approximate since any determination as to where the Sea Bank ends and the contiguous tidal river banks begin is necessarily subjective. Another old sea bank, known erroneously like this one as the Roman Bank, extends northwards up the Lincolnshire coast from Skegness, but it is not part of the fenland sea defences round the Wash and is probably of later origin, and is therefore considered to be an entirely different structure.

The Sea Bank's earthwork varies considerably in height and cross-section from place to place. At some locations the bank has disappeared entirely, in others it is up to 10ft or more in height. Public roads, lanes and tracks run along its crest for considerable distances and in a number of places (for example, Holbeach Clough and Gedney Dyke in Lincolnshire) linear village settlements have become established along its line. Its route is also characterised by numerous associated place-names, such as Holbeach Bank, Four Gotes, Tydd Gote, Lutton Gowts and Moulton Seas End, and numerous local names such as Bank Farm, Bank House, Banklands, etc. A gote or gowt is the same as a clough or sluice; tidal sluices would have been necessary on the line of the bank to allow flood water from the land to drain out to sea at low tide. The land on the seaward side is often higher than inland, due to warping by the tides after the bank's construction.

The hypothesis that the Wash's sea banks were Roman seems to have been started by the historian Sir William Dugdale in the 17th century, and uncritically repeated by subsequent antiquaries until the 1930s when C.W. Phillips and G. Fowler pointed out that there was no archaeological evidence whatsoever for ascribing Roman origins to the 'Roman Bank'. It is not inconceivable that the Romans did erect some sea defences along the shores of the Wash but certainly not the 'Roman Bank' as we now see it.

The Sea Bank has close archaeological associations with the chain of pre-Conquest Saxon villages along the silt ridge that fringes the north-west and south-west shores of the Wash, lying between the sea shore and the inundated peat fen inland. Strong evidence for the Sea Bank's pre-Conquest origin can be deduced from the relative positions of the bank and the adjacent early salterns (salt evaporation pans). The earliest documentary reference to the Sea Bank is in 1182 when Prior Garsinus of Spalding charged a priest with responsibility for repairing a section of the bank at Weston.

Although the Sea Bank's origins are fairly certainly pre-Conquest (it is known, for example, that the minor estuary of Fleet Haven had already been banked across by 1086), current academic opinion is that it was a piecemeal enterprise carried out in each parish by local landowners and/or the Church. Nevertheless, no part of such a sea defence work could function in isolation; each section would have to link up with those constructed by the parishes on either side. A considerable degree of collaboration and co-ordination would have been essential and the whole structure can therefore be considered as a single engineering work. Small-scale but progressive land reclamation took place during the 13th century and the line of the bank as seen today is its final late 13th-century position. The Black Death (1349-52) can be assumed to have halted further seaward progress during the Middle Ages and it seems that, for some reason, no further significant reclamation took place until the process recommenced in the mid-17th century and again more recently from the early 19th century.

The Sea Bank would certainly have been breached by the action of the North Sea storm tide surges at various times during its history. One such was the storm tide of 1571 immortalised in Jean Ingelow's poem 'High Tide on the Coast of Lincolnshire' when a breach occurred near Fosdyke. Until the 19th century it was customary in the fens to repair breached sea or river banks by constructing a new section of bank in an arc behind, rather than directly across, the breach. The resulting sudden kink in the line of the flood bank is still known as a 'gull' or 'horseshoe'. (HEW 1946)

WEST NEWTON
N23. Appleton Water Tower (TF 705277) is a highly ornate water tower of distinguished provenance. The condition of the water at Sandringham House, the Norfolk residence recently purchased by the Prince of Wales, was inquired into by the Rivers Pollution Commission in 1871, and all the waters obtained were pronounced unsafe and unfit for human consumption. It was also inadequate in quantity. The well from which it was obtained was 14ft below the offices. As a result, (Sir) Robert Rawlinson (who had been chairman of the Commission and was now Chief Engineering Inspector to the Local Government Board) was commissioned to advise on remedial measures. He in turn consulted Messrs Lawson & Mansergh of Westminster, who carried out the design of the new works to give a proper supply and also to provide a proper sewerage for the house and estate.

After several trial borings had been made, a supply from a spring about 1½ miles south-east of the house was decided upon. The spring was about +92ft O.D., about 22ft below the ground floor of the house, and there was an intervening ridge about 83ft higher than the spring, and five feet higher than the roof of the house. In order to store the water to give an adequate pressure for fire fighting, a water tower 60ft high was erected on the ridge.

A pumping station was constructed near Appleton Farm, where the water was softened by the addition of lime water, then pumped up a four-inch-diameter rising main 600 yards to the tank on the water tower. The lift from the bottom of the well to the tank was 175ft. The cast-iron tank, like the tower it sits on, was octagonal in plan, 24ft across and 12ft deep; its capacity was 32,000 gallons. It was supported by jack arches which themselves rested on two main and six cross-girders of cast iron. The base of the tank consisted of 49 plates, of which the central, octagonal, one carried a 12in-diameter hollow pipe that doubled as a support to the roof and a flue to the accommodation in the tower. It also served to provide heat to the tank in times of frost. The sides of the tank were formed by 120 plates in five tiers, the joints staggered as in brickwork. The roof was of timber, covered with lead. A manhole gave access to the top of the roof, which had a cast-iron railing round its perimeter. The tower was built with brick, on a base of red stone from Mansfield and the local brown carrstone. From the tank to the Hall the supply main was 1,870 yards long, six inches in diameter.

161 *Appleton Water Tower, West Newton.*

Sandringham was connected to the national supply c.1948, and this private supply was discontinued. Maintenance of the pumping station ceased, but a proposal to scrap it met with resistance. As a result, it was decided to donate the engine to the Ironbridge Gorge Museum in Shropshire. It was removed (which necessitated the demolition of the engine house) in 1979, and it has been on display at Ironbridge since 1995. The tower was bought by the Landmark Trust and is available for let as holiday accommodation. (HEW 2703)

WEST WALTON

N24. Kinderley's Cut (TF 4616 to TF 4720) was the first major improvement to the outfall of a Fenland river. In early times the River Nene flowed into a wide estuary immediately below Wisbech, a fact that can be seen by the location of the **Old Sea Bank (N22)**. The channel of the river changed course frequently as it became obstructed by silt brought down or sand washed in by the tide. Despite this, at least from the 11th century, ships, large for the time, were able to berth at quays alongside the river. This trade ceased abruptly in 1260 after a tidal surge wreaked havoc. From about this time, too, the waters of the Ouse found their way to Lynn, where the citizens obtained a charter from the king to secure the river in its new course. The construction of **Morton's Leam (C18)** from 1480 created a better flow of the River Nene to the town and the port was re-established. Despite continuing problems with floods from above and below, the port continued; dredging of the channel at least from 1635 moved the head of the estuary two miles below the town. However, the drainage of the lands around the river above the town, and particularly the North Level, was most unsatisfactory. Within the estuary the river was free to move its channel and in 1720 it swung over to the Norfolk shore, leaving Gunthorpe Sluice stranded quarter of a mile away. As this was the outfall of the Shire Drain, the main drain of the North Level, some action was necessary to restore the channel to its old line. After taking advice and getting contrary opinions, including opposition from Wisbech who feared that navigation to the town would be harmed, the Bedford Level board decided on 1 June 1721 to make a new cut through the marshes past the sluice and to construct training works so that its line would be maintained. Work started very soon after under the direction of Nathaniel Kinderley, who had been one of the parties consulted and who had earlier that year published a book in which he maintained that 'the main thing wanting for sure draining is good outfalls'. By June 1722 work was well advanced and the dam to cut off access to the old channel was under construction when rioters from Wisbech destroyed it by main force. The town's Corporation then obtained an injunction from the Lord Chancellor forbidding any further work.

For the next 50 years the drainage authorities, the Bedford Level Corporation until 1753 and then the newly independent North Level, were obliged to make do with cleaning out the internal drains and some improvements, of which Smith's Leam, 1728-30, was probably the most important. Their efforts were of little avail, however, and conditions in the Level continued to deteriorate. In 1751 Nathaniel Kinderley jr published a second, updated, edition of his father's book. In 1753 much of the Level was under a foot of water and the banks of the Nene were breached by floods in 1763, 1765 and 1767. The commissioners were thus driven to go back to Kinderley's ideas, and over the next four years consulted several eminent engineers, including John Smeaton, James Brindley, Thomas Yeoman, John Golborne and Langley Edwards. After another bad breach of the river in the winter of 1770 the commissioners resolved to bring the matter to a head and an Act for a part of Kinderley's scheme was passed towards the end of 1771. This would have allowed a tax borne in part by the people of Wisbech, who as usual objected strongly, so after negotiations in which John Grundy of Spalding played a part, a new Act was passed in 1773 that put the financial burden mainly on the North Level. The new channel was agreed to be called Kinderley's Cut in honour of its progenitor.

The channel was to be 100ft wide at the top, 40ft wide at the bottom and eight feet deep. Its end was to be protected by stone flagging and a bank to be constructed 60ft away on the east side would also be protected on its outer (sea) side. Work began soon after 9 August 1773 and the excavation was complete by June 1774. A dam to prevent the river from flowing down the old channel was necessary. It was to be formed of two banks of stone 120ft apart with earth and flagging between as an impermeable core. It was to rise to one foot above low water mark, presumably so that tides could overflow and the ground be warped. However when the first bank had been raised the tide flowed so rapidly over it that the ground was scoured away and threatened to undermine the bank. It was then hurriedly raised, and the whole dam complete by October 1774. Work on slope protection continued until summer 1776, when the works had cost about £9,000.

The effects on the river were quite dramatic. It scoured out a depth of 15 to 16ft and increased its width to 160ft. The level at Gunthorpe Sluice was lowered by six feet, the river at Wisbech by three feet and at Peterborough, 25 miles above, by two feet. Nearly 7,500 acres of land were reclaimed and passed to the commissioners as some recompense for their efforts. The scheme's success led to calls for similar improvements to other rivers leading into the Wash, though these, too, would be subject to detailed argument over many years before they were implemented.

Above the Cut there was a loop of the river to the Norfolk (east) side. From 1827 to 1829, when many poor people in the area were thrown on the parish, it was decided to employ them in making another cut to eliminate this loop. Properly called Woodhouse Marsh Cut, it was popularly known as Paupers' Cut. Money ran out before the work was completed and William Swansborough was consulted. After (Sir) William Cubitt had endorsed his plans, work was resumed with Swansborough in charge. Great difficulty was encountered in damming off the old channel – the contractor failed and when an attempt was made with direct labour on 7 May 1832 the incoming tide almost swept the day's work away. Work was resumed immediately and by nightfall enough had been done to preserve the dam. (HEW 2659)

WIGGENHALL

N25. Eau Brink Cut (TF 590149 to TF 613188) was a major river improvement with a lengthy gestation period. Below Wiggenhall St Germans the River Great Ouse took a circuitous course, with a wide curve to the west before swinging back to flow out at King's Lynn. By taking this lengthy detour, the gradient of the river bed was shallower than it would have been had the course been more direct. This stretch of the river was also much wider than the lengths upstream, so that the depth of water here could be as little as 14in, compared with five feet above. To improve the drainage of the lands above Wiggenhall St Germans, whose waters then flowed into the River Great Ouse at Welches Dam and Salter's Lode, Nathaniel Kinderley in 1721 suggested a new cut from Wiggenhall to West Lynn to straighten the line of the river. This cut would have the same width as the river above, so that its depth would be similar and the navigation would be preserved. Humphry Smith reported in 1729 and Kinderley again in 1730, but no action was taken at this time.

There followed over the next 70 years a series of reports by experienced engineers, arguing the case for and against the idea. The proponents claimed that it would increase the flow in the river, allowing more water to pass in times of flood and thus improve the drainage of the lands in the Middle and South Levels. Opponents alleged that the existing river, up to half a mile wide, acted as a reservoir that filled with each incoming tide, which then acted on the ebb to scour out the channel past King's Lynn and so preserve the navigation to the port. Those for the cut included William Elstobb (1777), John Golborne (1777), Robert Mylne (1792) and George Maxwell (1793). In 1791

162 *Eau Brink Cut. The river formerly swung to the left here, past the modern pylons.*

John Watté, John Smeaton and James Golborne each produced detailed proposals with dimensions and estimates – Golborne's was from 208 to 240ft wide and cost £38,000. The port interests rallied support from Sir Thomas Hyde Page (1775), Joseph Hodskinson (1793) and Joseph Nickalls (1793). In 1794, after serious floods had again demonstrated the need for a solution, Mylne and Page were appointed to submit detailed proposals. They were unable to agree on anything except the line of the cut, which was duly staked out, and on this basis an Act of Parliament was obtained in 1795. Still no action ensued, but in 1804 Joseph Huddart acted as umpire to try to settle the differences between Mylne and Page, tending rather towards the views of the former. He also settled the dimensions for the cut to be made. Matters dragged on until John Rennie sr was appointed to design the scheme, with Thomas Telford as his colleague to protect the navigation. The works were carried out in 1819-21 at a cost of about £312,610, with an immediate improvement to the drainage of the Levels. However the cross-section of the river proved inadequate in times of severe floods and in 1826-9 a further £33,000 was spent in widening the cut and improving the protection of the banks against erosion. (HEW 2658)

N26. Middle Level Main Drain (TF 505002 to TF 588142) gave an improved drainage to a large area of the Fens. The Bedford Level had first been drained effectively by two campaigns undertaken for the Earl of Bedford and his 13 co-Adventurers in 1640-1 and 1650-5. The area that became known as the Middle Level – that between the Old Bedford River and Smith's Leam, about 140,000 acres of low-lying land – drained to the River Great Ouse (Old Bedford River) at Welches Dam (TL 469858) and Salter's Lode Sluice (TF 586015). This drainage was not entirely satisfactory and the wet summer, autumn and winter of 1841 caused the rivers to swell so much that the pumps were unable to discharge the water from the local drains. On 27 April 1842 James Walker (President, ICE) was commissioned to report on all aspects of the problem. He and his partner Alfred Burges designed a new artificial cut to carry the waters to an outfall further down the Great Ouse at Wiggenhall St Germans, where the sill of a sluice could be about 2.5m below that at Salter's Lode. Though originally intended to extend 31 miles from Caldecot Farm (TF 174888) on the west side of (the former) Whittlesey Mere, in fact only 11¼ miles were constructed, from Three Holes (TF 505002), the junction of Popham's Eau and the Sixteen-Feet River to Wiggenhall, during 1844-7. The drain was inclined at one inch in a mile and was 30ft wide at its upper end, 40ft at the crossing with Well Creek and 50ft at its outfall; the side slopes were at one in two. At the outfall a sluice was constructed with three openings of 20ft each; its sill was eight feet below low water in the river.

In 1848 it was decided to deepen almost all of the main rivers and drains of the Level, about 110 miles, the exceptions being Well Creek, the Old River Nene, the Old Bedford River and King's Dyke. Several short new cuts were made to bring water more directly into the Main Drain. At the same time the crossing of the Well Creek, which was effected initially by sluices designed to maintain the level of water in the creek for navigation, was altered and an aqueduct was constructed to carry the creek over the drain. These works were completed by 1852.

For reasons of economy the drain was constructed less deep than Walker & Burges had proposed. In 1857 it was further decided to make it four feet deeper, which was carried out progressively upwards. In 1862 the sluice at the drain's outfall failed (**N27**) and within a few days, despite great efforts to strengthen the banks, they were breached.

Like all other principal drains in the fens, it is necessary to maintain the Middle Level Main Drain regularly, but unlike many others it remains substantially as it was

163 *Middle Level Main Drain).*

constructed. The timber bridges across it have been rebuilt in concrete and the aqueduct carrying the Well Creek over the drain at Mullicourt was replaced in 1921. (HEW 2656)

N27. Middle Level Outfall Sluice (TF 588142) had a chequered early history. As part of the **Middle Level Main Drain (N26)** works in 1844-7, a sluice was constructed at the drain's outfall into the River Great Ouse at Wiggenhall St Mary. Designed by James Walker, it had three openings of 20ft each and its sill was eight feet below low water in the river. Regrettably it blew up on 4 May 1862 and the tidal water flowed strongly up and down the drain. Steps were immediately taken to strengthen the banks of the drain but to no avail; after some days the western bank gave way about four miles above the sluice and about 6,000 acres of land were flooded. Fortunately the Marshland banks stood and the flood spread no further. While a solution was being found, old drains were cleaned out and reopened so that the rest of the Level could be drained via Salter's Lode Sluice, as had been the case before the Main Drain was constructed.

Walker was consulted immediately, but being old and in poor health (he died later in the year) he was unable to act, and (Sir) John Hawkshaw was commissioned to do all that was necessary to shut out the tide. His solution was a piled cofferdam – two rows

164 *Mullicourt Aqueduct.*

of sheet piles 25ft apart down the upper parts of the banks and twin whole baulks seven inches apart at 7ft 6in centres across the central 88ft, with timber panels seven inches thick spanning between the main piles. Because of the urgency the works were let to John Towlerton Leather without a contract being signed. Much of the piling work could only be done for short periods each day when the tide rose to the level of the water above the dam and there was still water at the site. The lowest tier of panels was seven feet deep and pointed on the underside so that it could be driven into the bed of the drain. Upper panels were less deep. The current of water increased as the gap narrowed and particular care was necessary to avoid scour. The first attempt to close the dam, on 10 June 1862, was a failure as three of the main piles gave way, allowing the panels between to be displaced. After new piles had been driven and repairs done, the second attempt, on 19 June, was successful. Further strengthening works included a complete row of sheet piles across the drain below the cofferdam and large quantities of clay being thrown in to provide a seal.

165 *Middle Level Main Drain Siphon under construction, 1862 (*Illustrated London News*).*

Subsequently 16 cast-iron siphons were laid over the top of the dam to allow the water from the Middle Level to pass down to the Great Ouse. There was a flap valve at the outlet of each to exclude the tidal waters and valves at the inlets allowing the siphons to be filled with water if necessary. Usually, however, the siphon was activated by means of a steam engine, connected by a pipe to the top of each siphon, which evacuated the air and drew the water up to start the flow. After the dam had been closed it was possible to repair the breach in the bank with clay and clunch, and the banks made good where scour had taken place. The flooded area was drained via the Marshland Smeeth Lode.

Although Hawkshaw had expected that the siphons would provide a permanent solution, continuing shrinkage of the land in the Level and silting of the drain caused by inadequate scour made a new sluice necessary after 14 years. Designed by Hawkshaw, it was constructed within a new bypass channel round the 1862 dam. It had three openings

166 *Middle Level Sluice, Wiggenhall St Germans (1934).*

of 17ft each and pointing doors that opened and closed automatically with the tide. It was completed in 1877. The plaque placed on the bridge over the channel when the sluice was opened remains *in situ* (TF 588140).

This in turn became less effective as deterioration in the estuary of the Great Ouse and shrinkage of the lands in the Level caused the hydraulic gradient to decrease. Gravity drainage was no longer sufficient by itself, so in 1928 a scheme to build a new sluice in the original line of the Main Drain and to provide it with pumps was approved as part of the national unemployment relief programme. The works were constructed by direct labour in 1930-4, with at least three-quarters of the workforce being drawn from the distressed areas and all of the equipment being of British manufacture. There are two sluices, each 35ft wide, centrally placed with a pumping station on each side. At first there were two sets of 1,000bhp diesel engines driving Gwynne's pumps in the north station and one set in the south; a fourth, more powerful, set was installed in the south station in 1951. The engines in the north station were replaced by electric motors in 1970, and the original engine in the south station replaced by one of 1,550bhp in 1981. The 1862 structure was removed to allow the waters to flow to the new station.

Now a new sluice/pumping station is being built downstream from the 1934 structure. It is being constructed within a cofferdam the full width of the Main Drain, so to allow the drain to remain operational a temporary bypass channel has been constructed around the south side of the site. The new works are due to be commissioned in 2010. (HEW 2657)

WIVETON

N28. Wiveton Bridge (TG 044427) is a medieval bridge with a large span for its time. Its single stone arch spans 32ft and rises 7ft 6in. The first known reference to it was in 1482, when there was a chapel beside it, and the present structure is almost certainly the one that existed then. The length of the span was quite ambitious, and it is supported by five chamfered ribs; other ribbed examples in Norfolk are at Newton Flotman, where the spans are only 14ft, and Potter Heigham, even less. It was formerly of much greater importance than now as, until a timber

bridge was built downstream in 1739, it was the lowest crossing of the River Glaven. The present coast road, A149, was not built until 1824 under the Blakeney and Cley Enclosure Act of 1821 (**N5**). (HEW 1541)

167 *Wiveton Bridge.*

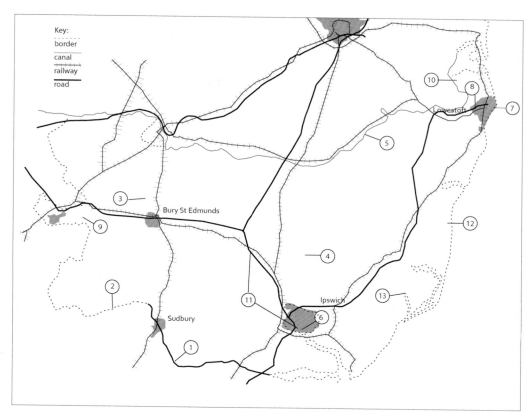

Map of Suffolk.

S1. Bures Bridge
S2. Priory Bridge, Clare
S3. Culford Bridge
S4. Helmingham Hall bridges
S5. Homersfield Bridge
S6. Ipswich Wet Dock
S7. Lowestoft Harbour

S8. Oulton Broad Swing Bridge
S9. Moulton Packhorse Bridge
S10. Herringfleet Windmill
S11. Ipswich & Stowmarket, or Gipping, Navigation
S12. Minsmere Level drainage
S13. Woodbridge Tidemill

BURES

S1. Bures Bridge (TL 906340) is a late but substantial cast-iron bridge. An earlier structure was found to be 'in a ruinous state' in 1508, when it was a wooden bridge owned by the Priory at Stoke-by-Clare. It is thought to have been rebuilt in 1679 as a masonry arch bridge and was known as Bures Great Bridge. The upkeep of the bridge devolved on a couple of landowners who were owners of the tithes, presumably descendants of people who acquired priory property at the dissolution of the monasteries. They sought to negotiate to release themselves from responsibility in 1879, when the bridge was said to be at least 200 years old. The tithe ownership came to an end with the building of the present bridge in 1881. The contractors were Rownson, Drew & Co. of London, whose only other known bridge is Meldon Viaduct in Devon.

168 *Bures Bridge.*

Bures Bridge has a single segmental cast-iron arch of 68ft span, carrying the B1508 over the River Stour. It has five ribs tapering from about 6ft 6in deep at the abutments to 1ft 2in at the crown of the arch, with Vierendeel-type open spandrels. The arch rises eight feet. There are brick abutments, with brick pilasters on the south side. The roadway has stone kerbs and a slight hump. There is a separate cast-iron kerb beam supporting cast fence posts with tubular rails.

In the 1950s a separate footbridge was erected along the north side to leave the maximum road width available for vehicles. After the main bridge had survived for almost a century, cracks in the face girders had to be repaired by the Metalock system in 1978. In 1991 strengthening was required to cope with the increased weights of modern traffic. This was effected by bonding steel plates to the undersides of the cast-iron ribs. (HEW 1643) There is a smaller version of the bridge at Wormingford, a few miles downriver.

CLARE

S2. Priory Bridge, Clare (TL 767449) is the largest of three bridges designed by (Sir) William Cubitt and cast by Ransome & Son at Ipswich in 1813-14. The others are at Brent Eleigh (1813) (TL 934483) and Saul's Bridge, Witham (1814) (TL 824139). Cubitt had joined the firm, then agricultural implement makers, in 1812 at the age of 27 and took charge of specialist iron castings. The opportunity to make his first road bridge came in the following year with the renewal of a small span carrying the Hadleigh to Bury St Edmunds road over the River Brett, about half a mile west of Brent Eleigh village. He chose a semi-elliptical profile for the 13ft span, with seven cast-iron ribs having a rise of three feet. A transverse rib binds the units at the crown of the arch, and through bolts are fixed at the mid-point of the spandrels. Cast-iron bearings on brick abutments (possibly remnants of the previous bridge) support the ribs and the soffit is lined with timber planks between the ribs to hold the concrete fill. On the face units, raised figures show the date 1813. The bridge cost £648 and from a document of the time evidently made a handsome profit for the firm.

In 1953 the road was diverted past the bridge to ease the curve and to eliminate the restrictive deck width of 13ft. The old bridge is now almost concealed among the bushes and the abutments are failing although the cast-iron ribs are still in sound condition.

Priory Bridge has three elliptical arches, spanning 11ft, 13ft 6in, 11ft, not large even for relatively early cast iron. As at Brent Eleigh, it has the date '1813' cast marked at the crown of the arch and there are seven ribs, though here there is an extra rib on the west face with cantilevered brackets to allow the road to splay out at the southern end. It was probably a late amendment to the design. The parapet railings end in short brick wing walls that have cast-iron capping marked 'Ward & Silver Melford'. It carries a minor road over the River Stour and is probably the easiest of the three bridges at which to park and inspect the bridge.

169 *Priory Bridge, Clare.*

Saul's Bridge carries the B1018 road over the River Brain, which is little more than a stream at this point, and is situated about half a mile south of Witham. Constructed in 1814, it was the second cast-iron bridge to be built in Essex and the oldest remaining in the county. The first, a bridge over the River Lea, was erected in 1810 by the Commercial Road Trust but was demolished during the industrial development of the Lea Valley.

In 1814, Robert Lugar, the Essex county surveyor, called for quotations to rebuild the defective bridge. He had intended to build a brick span but selected Ransome's design-and-build structure at a cost of £700 even though it was not the lowest tender. The success of this bridge led to the wider adoption of this method and material for road bridges in the county. The deck is made up of seven arched cast-iron ribs of 18ft span and two ornamental cast-iron parapet ribs, with cast plates resting on the lower flanges of the ribs. The ribs are supported on cast-iron bearer plates on brick abutments. The original cast-iron parapet fence remains on the east side but that on the west side was removed when the bridge was widened in 1955 with a reinforced concrete slab to carry the footpath. (HEWs 1362, 1642 and 1689)

CULFORD

S3. Culford Hall Bridge (TL 828704) is a structurally sophisticated cast-iron bridge, the only example known of a design to a patent taken out by Samuel Wyatt in June 1800. It takes a driveway from Culford Hall (now Culford School) over a lake dug in 1795, but the bridge was not built until 1803-4.

The distinctive feature of the patent is that the main ribs are twin hollow tubular sections with end plates and a central spacer between them. There are six ribs, each made up of five sections. The end plates are oval and abut onto perforated transverse plates that provide lateral rigidity. Solid plates continue above the outer ribs; these and arched deck plates above the ribs contain the unmade roadway. The castings were provided by William Hawks jr of Gateshead, County Durham, at a cost of £1,457. The abutments are of granite and the parapet balusters are made of composition stone. The bridge has a clear span of 60ft and an overall length of 108ft; the roadway is 13ft wide.

It is the 10th oldest surviving cast-iron bridge in Britain and marks an interesting attempt to exploit the properties of cast iron in a rational way. That no other bridges to Wyatt's patent are known to have followed it may be due to the difficulties and expense of casting hollow tubes of this profile. It can be seen from a public footpath that runs through the school grounds north of the bridge. (HEW 2076)

170 *Culford Hall Bridge.*

171 *Helmingham Hall East Bridge.*

HELMINGHAM

S4. Helmingham Hall bridges (TM 187577) are two graceful and intricate cast-iron bridges crossing the south-east and north-east arms of the 60ft-wide moat surrounding Helmingham Hall. John Nash, the celebrated Regency architect, was retained to design major alterations to the Hall and his proposals with a strong Tudor-Gothic flavour were illustrated on drawings which he exhibited at the Royal Academy in 1800. One of his drawings shows a rather frail-looking bridge of three equal cast-iron spans to replace the earlier brick arch bridge. In the event, the bridges are more substantial structures with a main semi-elliptical arch of 31ft 6in and a side span with a nine-foot pointed arch to balance the span of a timber drawbridge at the inner side of the moat. The two drawbridges are still raised every night as they have been since 1510.

The vertically strutted spandrels of the three cast-iron ribs, with Gothic flourishes, are reflected in the decorated openwork cast-iron balustrades; cast-iron cross-girders at three-foot centres with brick jack arches support brick-paved roadways, though that on the south-east side leading to the main entrance has a tar and gravel surfacing. 'Ransome Ironfounder Ipswich' is cast onto the main girders. Two original (1760) 13ft-high brick obelisks flank the approach to the bridge.

The date of these bridges is uncertain; neither Ransome's nor Helmingham Hall archives appear to have any records of their construction. Although dates as early as *c.*1800 have been ascribed to them, they almost certainly owe nothing to Nash. They were probably a design-and-build project by Ransome's, whose first cast-iron bridges were made in 1813 (**S2**). The bridges at Helmingham are altogether more assured than those, and their architectural style is similar to Ransome's Stoke Bridge at Ipswich of 1818 (now demolished), though that had solid spandrels rather than the open ones at Helmingham. A date of the latter period seems likely. (HEW 0341)

172 *Homersfield Bridge.*

HOMERSFIELD

S5. Homersfield Bridge (TM 283857) is the oldest existing concrete bridge in Britain. There are few remaining examples of early attempts to combine iron and concrete in bridge construction before the era of true reinforced concrete, but a remarkable survivor is the 50ft span over the River Waveney at Homersfield on the county boundary of Suffolk and Norfolk. Built in 1870 for the owner of Flixton Hall Estates, Sir Shafto Adair, it has a wrought-iron lattice frame fully encased in concrete. There is an armorial crest at the centre of the span. The monolithic arch, segmental in profile, rises five feet and tapers from a depth of 6ft 4in at the haunches to 2ft 3in at the crown. It was designed by H.M. Eyton, an Ipswich architect, and the span was constructed by W. & T. Phillips of London at a cost of £344.

The bridge once carried the B1062 but the road was diverted over a new bridge in the early 1970s and the old one now remains open to pedestrians only. By the 1980s the bridge had deteriorated quite badly, but it has now been refurbished. In earlier days the Flixton Estate hung a chain between the flamboyantly decorated balustrades on one day each year and charged a toll of a penny per wheel for vehicles to cross the bridge. (HEW 0836)

IPSWICH

S6. Ipswich Wet Dock (TM 168433) was the first in East Anglia. Ipswich has had a port since at least the 13th century, when a Common Quay was probably in existence. By the 18th century, however, the river had dried out by the Common Quay at low water and vessels larger than eight feet draught had to unload three miles downstream. The end of the 18th century saw an upturn in fortunes and the merchants and businessmen of the town sought advice from William Chapman, an engineer from Newcastle-upon-Tyne who had experience in inland waterways. He made his first report in 1797.

By the beginning of the 19th century the Committee of Subscribers for the Improvement of the Port of Ipswich, to whom Chapman had submitted his reports, could not delay action any longer. The population of 12,124 in 1755 had fallen to 11,061 by 1801 and the town's industries were being held back by the river's decline. On 15 February 1803 a general meeting of Ipswich inhabitants agreed to seek Chapman's advice again, following which his third report of 1804 offered two plans for deepening the river and straightening it to allow vessels of 250 tons to reach the quay at spring tides. He pointed out that although the plan would cost £15,000, continuing expenditure would be needed for dredging, which was allied to Ipswich Corporation's monopoly on supplying ballast to ships leaving empty. The inhabitants and the Corporation each set up committees to consider a bill for Parliament. The Corporation proposed that all 41 of their members should be River Commissioners, leaving only 25 commissioners for the inhabitants. The latter were not convinced that the Corporation had their best interests at heart, so the Committee of Subscribers went ahead with its own bill. Not surprisingly the Corporation objected to the bill when it was presented, but their previous record went against them and the Act for 'improving and rendering more commodious the Port of Ipswich in the County of Suffolk' went through all its stages and received royal assent in 1805. Steam dredgers were introduced the following year, and in 1819 and 1821 new cuts were made through loops in the river through Round Ooze and from Lime Kiln Reach to Hog Island Reach, the latter one under (Sir) William Cubitt.

The ships using the port were not large but still needed pilots to negotiate the channel. At a public meeting on 19 January 1836 it was proposed 'to take into consideration a proposal for forming a Wet Dock at this Port and improving the River and Harbour'. A plan was proposed by William Lane, the Collector of Customs for the port, to form the existing channel from St Peter's Dock to the Ballast Wharf into a wet dock, and bypass it by a cut to carry the tidal water, repeating a suggestion that had been put forward earlier by William Chapman. The meeting appointed a Dock Committee, and help was sought from Henry Palmer, a vice-president of the Institution of Civil Engineers, to report on the viability of a wet dock allowing ships to stay afloat at all tidal states. His plan, ambitious for its time, comprised a dock of 33 acres water area, the largest in Britain, all of the existing Thames docks as well as those at Liverpool, Hull and Leith being smaller. The Dock Committee proceeded with the preparation of a parliamentary bill to enable a new body of commissioners to raise the money. At the eleventh hour a group of River Commissioners tried to stop the bill, but they were defeated at a meeting on 19 June 1837; it was their final meeting, and the Ipswich Dock Act passed on 30 June 1837.

Henry Palmer considered three schemes, one was Chapman's with a canal and dock, one was for a dam downriver to make an enormous dock, and one was William Lane's. His proposal was a combination of Chapman's and Lane's and the plans were ready by 23 October 1837, the work estimated at £58,100. Tenders were invited and the lowest tender of £65,178 from David Thornbury of King's Lynn was accepted in March 1838. The contract was signed on 12 June 1838, digging work having begun three days earlier. The work specified included the construction of the Wet Dock to give 17ft depth at spring tides to enable ships of about 400 tons to stay afloat at all times; embankments each end to contain the water; a new channel for the waters of the Gipping; a lock 140ft long by 45ft wide to gain access to the dock, a 30ft quay on the north side to allow passage of vehicles along the waterside, and a new sewer under the quay to discharge Ipswich's drainage into the Orwell. This last was a particularly tricky aspect of the work. On 26 June 1839 the foundation stone of the new lock was laid; a dinner was held in it on 1 October for the workmen to celebrate the completion of that part. By early 1840 the New Cut work was nearly complete, still being separated from the river by dams at each end. The lock gates were operated for the first time on 17 January 1842. The river was dredged to 16ft from near Cliff Quay (upstream from the present Orwell Bridge) to near Woolverstone and a new channel created in 1845-7. The final cost had escalated, figures of £110,000 and £130,000 being given.

The original entrance lock had been constructed at an angle of 45 degrees with the New Cut, which made negotiation into the Wet Dock for the increasingly large ships more and more difficult. Sufficient controversy had been aroused after several incidents with ships to accelerate the proposal of a new lock at the southern end of the dock, 300ft long and 50ft wide, and capable of taking 18ft draught vessels, in line with the river. The bill having passed through Parliament in 1877, the contract for the new lock and swing bridge over the lock was awarded to Henry Lee & Son of London for £45,000. Work began in June 1879 and it was opened on 27 July 1881. Two sets of gates were installed and provision made for a third set of outward-opening gates to keep out abnormal high tides. The swing bridge, which had provision for the railway to make a complete circuit of the dock, was not fitted until 1903. The third set of gates was eventually fitted in 1976 as part of Anglian Water's Ipswich Flood Prevention scheme.

The 20th century saw several improvements, including the construction of the 800ft-long ferroconcrete South-West Quay and Timber Quay on the south-east side of the island site next to New Cut in 1904, and the creation of ferroconcrete End Quay and Tovells Wharf on the north side of the island site in 1923-4, which were created by filling in the branch Dock where the original lock had been. In 1965 the Public Warehouse Quay on the north side of the Wet Dock was rebuilt. The swing bridge across the lock was replaced in 1949 by Ransomes & Rapier, allowing main line access to Cliff

Quay. More recent developments have involved wholesale rebuilding of the dockside. (HEW 2622)

LOWESTOFT

S7. Lowestoft Harbour (TM 549927) is the result of several phases of construction, from 1827 to 1906. The original harbour at Lowestoft was created in 1827-31 by the **Norwich & Lowestoft Navigation (N10)**. The works in Lowestoft included a lock at Mutford Bridge with gates facing both ways to allow for differences in level, as high tide on each side differed by about three hours; a sea lock with a swing bridge over it; and piers to channel the outflow in an attempt to keep the entrance channel open by scour. The sluices at the sea lock were effective enough at first, but the benefits did not extend far enough seaward to prevent the formation of a bar outside the piers. Then more frequent admission of tidal water to Lake Lothing to allow more frequent sluicing allowed silt in the sea water to be deposited in the lake and the channel through it slowly decreased in depth. There had been a small improvement under new local ownership from 1842, who then sold the Navigation to (Sir) Samuel Morton Peto in October 1844.

Peto, by then a well-established railway contractor, had the previous month purchased the nearby estate of Somerleyton, and almost immediately promoted a railway from Lowestoft to Reedham, where it would join the Yarmouth & Norwich Railway. The Engineer for the line was Robert Stephenson, though the actual work was done by his partner, George Bidder. The railway was part of a larger scheme by Peto to control a line of communication from the north of England to the Continent by rail and sea, with Lowestoft harbour as the point of interchange. A bill for the railway and for a new, larger, harbour outside the existing one was presented to Parliament and the Lowestoft Railway & Harbour Act was passed in 1845. It was leased from the outset by the Norfolk Railway, in which Peto had an influential stake.

173 *Lowestoft Harbour.*

The railway was built by Grissell & Peto under a conventional contract for about £80,000. James Hodges, who had worked for (Sir) William Cubitt on the South Eastern Railway, was agent in charge of the works which included the swing bridges at Somerleyton and Reedham. The line was opened on 3 May 1847. Later Hodges became agent for Peto, Brassey & Betts on the great Victoria Bridge on the Grand Trunk Railway of Canada.

It appears that the harbour works were constructed by Hodges using direct labour. The principal works were two new piers extending further out to sea than the 1832 structures and overlapping them. Piling started on 1 May 1846 and was complete by August 1847; some infilling with stone continued for a while. The cost was over £205,000. The opening of the railway brought significant amounts of traffic to the port, and between 1851 and 1857 it was also served by Peto's Northern Steam Packet Co., which operated cargo and passenger services to Denmark.

In 1853-4 a large graving dock was built in the inner harbour to the design of Charles Cheffins. It was built by the Tredwells, a successful firm of railway contractors. It was a valuable facility, and was extensively rebuilt in concrete in 1928. It remains, though the nearby patent slipway for trawler repairs has been demolished.

174 *Lowestoft Dry Dock.*

In 1872 the fish market was extended to a site north of the outer north pier. To protect the fishing vessels from the eastern swell, the Trawl Dock was formed by building a pier back from the end of the outer pier nearly to the end of the inner pier, leaving only a space for entry to the dock. In 1882-3 the 1872 pier was truncated and much of the outer north pier removed in order to allow the creation of a large new dock to the north. Opened on 1 October 1883, it was called the Waveney Dock. At the same time a sea wall and groyne was built northwards from the end of the outer north pier to try to arrest the littoral drift that brought sand and shingle across the harbour entrance. They were not completely effective, as in 1888 and 1896 the entrance was completely blocked, requiring the company's dredgers to work overtime to clear a way through. The Trawl Dock, which had been reduced in size in order to provide access to the Waveney Dock, was extended westwards in 1893, and in 1896 the North Groyne was built in another attempt to divert the littoral drift. This, too, was not totally successful, as the harbour mouth was blocked again in 1918. The final major civil engineering work was the creation of the Hamilton Dock north of the Waveney, in 1906, although improvements to the quays of the inner harbour continued at least until the First World War. More recently, Lowestoft has reinvented itself as a base for North Sea construction, repair and maintenance facilities. (HEW 2714)

S8. Oulton Broad Swing Bridge (TM 522926) is an unusual cable-stayed railway swing bridge. Known as Carlton Colville Bridge when it was first built in 1848, it was one of six similar centrally pivoted cast-iron swing bridges designed by George Bidder for railways over navigable rivers and built between 1845 and 1857; the others were at Norwich Trowse, Reedham, Somerleyton, St Olaves and Beccles. Reedham and Somerleyton were completely rebuilt in 1904, Trowse in 1906 and Oulton Broad in 1907. St Olaves and Beccles were the last to be rebuilt, in 1924-6, but they have been demolished.

Oulton Broad Swing Bridge carries a double-line railway over Lake Lothing, which had been made navigable as part of the **Norwich & Lowestoft Navigation (N10)** in 1829. The swing span is 120ft long, with steel plate girders, cross-girders and rail-bearers.

A central portal 23ft long, 19ft high, has three-inch-diameter tie rods passing over it to the main girder ends, making it effectively a cable-stayed structure. It provides clear openings of 44ft, one of which is navigable, and there are fixed side spans of 45ft and 30ft. The substructure dates from the 1907 rebuilding, as the new bridge was built 28ft away from the old.

The second Trowse Bridge had a superstructure like that here at Oulton Broad, but it was rebuilt again in 1987 as part of the electrification of the London-Norwich main line. It was notable as the first swing bridge with overhead catenary on British Railways. The opportunity was also taken to move the pier to the south bank of the river and so increase the navigable width of the River Wensum. (HEW 0744)

MOULTON

S9. Moulton Packhorse Bridge (TL 697645) is thought to be the only genuine packhorse bridge in the region. It has four arches over the River Kennett that vary in span from 10ft 4in to 10ft 9in. The main facing to the bridge is constructed with knapped flints, but its sharp-pointed arches are turned in nine-inch red brickwork. The arches are 7ft 6in high and the bridge is steeply humped, narrowing from 10ft wide at the ends to five feet between the parapets in the centre. The parapets stand 2ft 4in above the modern surface, presumably low enough to allow free passage of laden pack horses over the bridge. No records remain of its building, but it is ascribed to the 14th or 15th century. The bridge lies on an old trade route between Cambridge and Bury St Edmunds. A paved ford alongside is provided for modern traffic.

There is another narrow bridge nearby, with a 19ft span but only four feet wide, at TL 698642. Its single segmental arch ring has chamfered limestone voussoirs, and the rest of the bridge is mainly of flint. This one may be late medieval, constructed as a footbridge for the benefit of the village.

175 Oulton Broad Swing Bridge, opening to river traffic.

176 Moulton Packhorse Bridge.

SOMERLEYTON

S10. Herringfleet Windmill (TM 466976), the last surviving example of its type, is a little smockmill, standing isolated on the bank of the River Waveney across open meadows half a mile from the B1074 road between Somerleyton in Suffolk and St Olaves in Norfolk. It was built as a pumping mill by Robert Barnes, a Yarmouth millwright, c.1820.

The three-storey timber smock tower is octagonal, with tarred weatherboarded sides each 6ft 6in wide at its base. Four common sails originally covered in cloth are mounted on a six-inch-diameter iron shaft with a wooden brakewheel meshing with an iron spurwheel. The boat-shaped cap has a braced tail pole to move cap and sails into the wind.

Inside the mill there are three floors, the ground floor being the spartan accommodation for the marshman, who would sometimes have spent all night at the mill if the weather demanded constant attention to the sails. From the brakewheel on the iron windshaft in the cap a stout vertical wooden shaft transmits the drive to the ground floor where a horizontal iron shaft turns an outside scoop wheel housed in a semi-circular casing. The 16ft-diameter iron scoop wheel with nine-inch-wide wooden paddles lifted water from a drainage channel some 10ft to discharge into the river.

The Somerleyton Estate kept the mill working until 1955 when the job of draining the marshes was taken over by an electric pump. Fortunately, Suffolk county council decided to restore and preserve the mill (on a long lease from Somerleyton Estate) and completed the restoration in 1958. The mill is still in working order and is operated occasionally for visiting parties. There is a small car park at TM 468982, but the path from there is not clearly marked; a more direct route is by the public footpath from TM 471979 but there is no obvious place to park. (HEW 0688)

STOWMARKET

S11. Ipswich & Stowmarket, or Gipping, Navigation. The River Gipping was navigated occasionally in medieval times, and a proposal was made in the early 18th century to

177 *Herringfleet Windmill.*

make it regularly navigable. That was dropped in the face of opposition from Ipswich Corporation, but later in the century the need for improved communication from Stowmarket down to Ipswich became more pressing. In 1789 William Jessop, then taking over from his old master, John Smeaton, as the leading canal engineer of the day, was commissioned by some local landowners to survey the valley and provide proposals for a navigation. Jessop was engaged at the same time with the River Thames, the Basingstoke Canal, the Cromford Canal and the Grand Canal in Ireland. In view of his work on the Gipping, it is interesting to note that he reported to the Thames commissioners that

> The making of walls at all in the chamber of a lock is not absolutely necessary: but without them the earth would be liable to be washed away, or the chamber by having too large a capacity would in canals waste much water, and where water is plentiful, will at least waste time in filling it.

The survey was made by Isaac Lenny, a surveyor from Norwich, and on the basis of his report, endorsed by Jessop, an Act was passed on 1 April 1790. It authorised works on the river from Stowupland Bridge, Stowmarket, to Handford Bridge, Ipswich, the upgrading of the River Orwell

178 *Baylham Lock under reconstruction, 2009.*

from there to Stoke Bridge in Ipswich and a lateral cut in Stowmarket to the turnpike road; this last was never made. The Act appointed six trustees, rather than creating a company of proprietors; they were empowered to borrow £14,300 and raise a further £6,000 by mortgaging the property, if required. The waterway, including the towpath, was to be no more than 18 yards wide, or 20 yards at winding places or where the banks were more than three feet high.

Following his usual practice, having helped steer the bill through Parliament, Jessop provided general drawings and specifications and then retired from the scene. On 17 June the trustees appointed James Smith of Reading 'Surveyor of the whole work in the navigation from Ipswich to Stowmarket with a salary of three hundred pounds' from 21 July 1790 to 1 October 1791 (by which time they expected the works to be completed),

> he to be constantly resident on the spot ... allowing to the said James Smith an absence of one week in each quarter of the year on his appointing a proper person to be approved by the Trustees to supply his place during that period, the salary to be paid quarterly.

On 17 April advertisements had been placed in the Oxford, Birmingham and Cambridge newspapers for contractors, to be sent in by 24 May. Tenders were received from Samuel Weston and Dyson & Pinkerton. Weston already had 20 years' experience both as engineer and contractor on the Chester, Leeds & Liverpool and the Oxford Canals. John Dyson had been active since 1767, mostly on large-scale drainage works; his partner George Pinkerton was a member of a family who had worked with Jessop on other canal projects. After some negotiations with the trustees, who wanted to alter the terms of the tender, Dyson & Pinkerton were awarded the contract on 3 July. Unfortunately, in their keenness to proceed with the work, the contractors entered onto lands that had not been purchased. A lawsuit ensued that put a stop to works at the Ipswich end for some time, and the dismissal of Dyson & Pinkerton on 26 October 1790. In early December, John Treacher, Surveyor of the Upper Districts of the River Thames where he, too, was associated with William Jessop, examined the contractors' work and valued it at £214 19s. 11d. They appealed against this and in an arbitration award dated 14 November 1791 Robert Mylne, the leading architect/civil engineer, awarded them £651 7s. od.; they received the outstanding balance on 24 January 1792, 15 months after they had been dismissed.

After the contractors left the site, Smith took over, presumably employing the late contractors' workforce to keep the works going where they were not affected by the litigation. Samuel Wright of Ipswich was contracted to build six locks between June 1791 and June 1792, and had probably completed Stowupland, Badley and Needham Locks within the first six months.

After the lawsuit had been settled on 14 November 1791, John Rennie was asked to survey the works. At the time he had been involved in several surveys for canals but had not yet taken any of them to construction. He spent three days going over the line and one week later, on 22 December, submitted his report to the trustees. He noted that the works from Stowmarket to Needham were nearly complete, and that the locks and bridges were of timber. While he agreed that local road bridges should continue thus, he recommended brick for public roads and the locks. It would be absolutely necessary to find a resident engineer who understood brickmaking and brick building. By this time the canal mania was gathering force, and he would endeavour, but could not promise, to find such a person. On 1 March 1792 Richard Coates, who had probably been a mason/contractor previously, was appointed at a salary of £200 p.a.; James Smith's accounts end on 24 March. By the middle of April, when Rennie visited the works again, John Hamer, a bricklayer, and James Wilkins, a carpenter, had arrived from the Basingstoke Canal to take charge of the structures.

It was now necessary to apply to Parliament for a further Act to raise another £15,000 and, with evidence from Rennie, this was passed on 28 March 1793. Work now proceeded rapidly, and the navigation was opened to traffic throughout on 14 September 1793. Richard Coates left on 29 October to work on the **Chelmer & Blackwater Navigation (E2)**, where Rennie was also the Engineer. Work on upgrading the Ipswich & Stowmarket, for instance mason's work at Handford and Claydon Bridges, continued until 1798 under George Coates, Richard's brother, who had until now been his assistant.

The navigation was a broad one, designed to take barges measuring up to 52ft 6in by 13ft 6in. The pre-existing watermills were bypassed. There were 15 locks, including the one at Handford into the tidal Orwell. There were no spectacular engineering works.

The navigation was leased to the Eastern Union, later the Great Eastern, Railway from 1846 to 1888, by which time there was very little traffic. By the 1920s the accumulated funds had disappeared and the trust was going deeper into debt. The navigation was effectively closed in 1932 and the last meeting of the trustees was held on 16 March 1934.

Conservation and restoration work has been going on intermittently since the 1970s. The Gipping Way, a footpath that follows the course of the river for much of its length, was established. Since 1994 Bosmere and Creeting Locks have been restored, and work is under way on Baylham Lock.

THEBERTON

S12. Minsmere Level drainage (TM 477661) was designed by William Smith, the 'Father of Geology'. The Level comprises 1,600 acres of low-lying land in the parishes of Leiston, Theberton, Dunwich, Westleton and Middleton with Fordley, bounded on the east side by the North Sea. There were protection works with an outlet sluice from at least the 18th century.

Under an Act of 1810 (50 George III c81), a body of local landowners was constituted a trust to improve the drainage. The fall from Rackford Bridge, Middleton, to the sea was eight feet, or 2ft 6in per mile. Whereas the Level had previously drained through a sluice near Coney Hill at the north end, a new river would take the water from East Bridge over the last 1½ miles more or less directly east to a new sluice further south. Another new drain would take water from an existing sheet of water called The Broad south-east to the new sluice and the existing stream running north parallel to and just behind the coastline to The Broad would be diverted into the sluice.

These works had been surveyed in 1808-9 by Anthony Bower, a surveyor of Lincoln who had worked as resident engineer with William Jessop on Holderness Drainage in 1792 and with John Rennie senior on the drainage of the East, West and Wildmore Fens in 1802-8. He was appointed Engineer to the Trustees at their first meeting on 7 June 1810, but he failed to attend subsequent meetings, pleading the need at different times to attend Quarter Sessions at Sleaford and Ely and other business in London. When he did manage to be present, on 3 January 1811, he had to admit that the plans were not available – they were being reviewed by Rennie, who was then in Ireland. Indeed it is clear that Rennie was closely involved – the draft contract for excavation is amended in his handwriting. The Trustees do not seem to have had much knowledge of the wider world of land drainage nor to have looked further than Bower for their expertise until a personal contact alerted them to William Smith, who was paying a visit to the neighbourhood. An approach was made and Bower was dismissed on 14 March 1811.

179 *Minsmere Level Sluice.*

Smith had been Sub-engineer of the Somersetshire Coal Canal in 1793-9, for which John Rennie senior was Engineer, and from 1800 had been a consulting engineer whose practice included land drainage and sea defences. He started design work afresh and it was not until 16 March 1812 that his plans were approved at a meeting of the trustees. A hexagonal well would receive the three drains through arches in its west, north-west and south-west faces respectively and a pipe would be laid from the east face, under the sandhills (known locally as benthills) along the shoreline to discharge the land water into the sea. As part of his agreement Smith was obliged to find a resident engineer, and he appointed John Godwin to the post. The beach is liable to move under the action of the waves, so to support the outfall Jacob Garrett of Ipswich proposed to supply cast-iron 'mushrooms' which would be driven down to firm ground below the shingle and on which the pipe would rest. Smith approved this and contracted with Garrett for their supply and installation. The trustees wanted local men to be employed for excavation and Smith contracted with Thomas Woods, Richard Butcher and Thomas Barrow for a drain across Leiston Common. Their performance must have been satisfactory as subsequent contracts were let to them. Works had advanced sufficiently by August 1813 for the trustees to arrange for surveys of the lands for enclosure, but work on the outfall continued through much of 1814. Godwin was made redundant on 27 October that year. By the end of 1815, £12,694 5s. 3½d. had been paid out.

In 1828 it was necessary to raise the sea banks at the north end of the level and a contract was made with a banksman, William Cleveland of Walberswick, to do so. In 1881 it was decided to add a second outfall pipe and the work was carried out by Andrew Handyside & Company of Derby. Although the tendency of the coastline is to erode, a large bank of shingle grew up in front of the benthills, which blocked the outlet. Further works in 1891, 1898-9 and 1911 included the lengthening of the outfall pipes. From about 1901 the benthills have been strengthened by faggots. Some concrete blocks are laid directly on the sand where the vegetation has been eroded. The hexagonal sluice still exists, beside a junction of public footpaths. Each face measures about 10ft 8in internally. The seaward end of the outfall is marked by a post, and the pipes' covering where they emerge from the beach is visible at most states of the tide.

Four drainage mills erected to lift water from the local drains into the New River have been demolished. One, called Eastbridge Windpump, was a smock mill built in the mid-19th century, probably by Robert Martin of Beccles. It was finally blown down during the winter of 1977/8, but the ironwork was salvaged and taken to the Museum of East Anglian Life at Stowmarket, where it has been rebuilt. Much of the Level has been allowed to revert to a marshy state and is administered as a nature reserve by the Royal Society for the Protection of Birds. (HEW 2694)

WOODBRIDGE

S13. Woodbridge Tidemill (TM 277485) is one of only three tidemills in Britain that have been restored to working order, the others being at Thorrington, Essex (**E11**) and Eling near Southampton. It is unusual in that the reservoir to hold the incoming tide is formed not by damming the head of a creek but is a pond formed by an embankment at one side of the estuary of the River Deben. There has been a mill on this site since before 1170. The present structure, together with a new warehouse and improvements to the quay alongside, was constructed in 1793. It continued to work, in an increasingly rickety state and with the assistance of a diesel engine in the last years, until 1957, when the wheel shaft broke. It was the last working tidemill in the country. After a further 11 years of neglect it was purchased for restoration and over the years 1971-6 the building was strengthened and the waterwheel and machinery were restored. The

180 *Woodbridge
Tidemill.*

original mill pond had been sold off to be used as a yacht marina and it was in 1982 that a smaller replacement was constructed to enable the mill to work again.

The mill is open daily from May to September and at weekends during the month before and after. As the new mill pond stores less water than the original, it only operates for about two hours at low tide, so visitors are recommended to consult the tide tables when planning a visit. There is an admission charge, and guidebooks are for sale. Parking space is available off Station Road and Quayside but not beside the mill. (HEW 0113)

abutment – the masonry at each end of the arch which provides the resistance to the thrust of the arch.

accumulator, hydraulic – a large vertical cylinder/piston to pressurise a water power system; a heavy weight is raised to the top of the piston and the system is pressurised by the weight operating under gravity.

agger – a raised causeway upon which a Roman road was constructed.

aqueduct – a bridge carrying a watercourse over another watercourse, road, railway or valley.

arch dam – of masonry or concrete, used where the rock formations at the sides of the valley are able to support the thrust from the arch form, providing a more economical material and capable of being built to greater heights. Sound rock is also needed for the foundations.

arch types:

> **elliptical** – similar to segmental but with the centre portion flattened;
>
> **pointed** – two half-segments with radii displaced to opposite sides of arch, meeting at the centre at a sharp point, can be sharp or flat;
>
> **relieving** – an arch built into a structure to reduce the load on a wall below;
>
> **semi-circular** – formed of one half of a circle, rise equal to half the span;
>
> **segmental** – formed of less than half a circle, rise less than half the span;
>
> **Tudor** – each side formed of a short vertical length leading to a sharp curved corner and an upward-angled straight length to the centre.

asphalt – a high-strength road material of stone and binder of bitumen or natural asphalt.

balanced cantilever construction – the bridge is built in increments each side of a support pier. Construction can be either by casting the increments *in situ* using specially designed shuttering to form the hollow concrete sections or by casting the sections off-site and transporting and lifting into place. The method is particularly useful where access to the land under the bridge is difficult. Also used for steel bridges.

bascule – a single- or double-leaf bridge usually over a waterway which can be pivoted about a horizontal axis to give a clear headroom for vessels to pass through.

bitumen – a by-product of distillation of crude petroleum oil.

box girder – a girder of rectangular or trapezoidal cross-section whose web and flanges are relatively thin compared with the space in the box.

bowstring girder – a girder with a straight bottom chord from which springs an arched top chord, the two connected by rigid stiffening members.

breast shot wheel – a water wheel which is supplied by water at about mid-height.

buck – the body of a post mill.

buttress dam – a development of the gravity dam with the downstream face supported by buttresses, reducing the amount of material necessary to resist the water pressure.

bye-wash – a channel which allows excess water to by-pass a lock.

cable-stayed bridge – a bridge whose deck is directly supported by a fan of cables from the towers.

cantilever – a beam not supported at its outer end.

cast iron – an iron-carbon alloy with impurities which preclude it being rolled or forged; it has to be poured in molten form into moulds of the required shape and size.

centering – a temporary structure to support an arch during building.

conduit – an artificial watercourse, either in pipe or open channel, to convey drinking water. Often used also for the fountain, pump or other outlet from which the water is drawn.

crowntree – a great transverse timber beam at the top of the post in a post mill which rotates the buck and the sails to face the wind.

cut and cover – a tunnel or part of a tunnel constructed by excavating a cutting to build it and then burying it; often used at the ends of a tunnel to reduce the amount of actual tunnelling required.

cutwater – a v-shaped upstream face of a bridge pier; designed to part the flow of water and prevent debris accumulating around the pier; sometimes provided also on the downstream face.

dentilation – ornamentation resembling teeth, used to decorate cornices.

dripmould – a projecting course of stone or brick designed to throw off rain.

edge rail – a rail without an upstanding flange as opposed to a plate rail (q.v.).

embankment dam – resists the water pressure by its weight. Can be of compacted earth or rockfill with a vertical impermeable central clay core to prevent seepage through the dam. This form is particularly suitable for wide flat valleys. Rockfill types can have an impermeable upstream face rather than a core.

Engineer – the engineer in charge of the project.

engineering brick – brick with greater crushing strength than common brick.

extrados – the exterior curve of an arch, measured on the top of the voussoirs.

falsework – a temporary structure to support the formwork (q.v.) for casting concrete.

formwork – (or shuttering), a temporary structure to contain wet concrete and form its finished shape until set and self-supporting.

gauge – the distance between the inner faces of the rails for edge rail track or the outer flanges for a plateway:
>   **standard gauge** – the track gauge of 4ft 8½in in general use in Britain;
>   **broad gauge** – a track gauge greater than standard, up to 7ft ¼in, used by Brunel;
>   **narrow gauge** – any gauge less than standard, usually around two feet.

girder – a beam formed by connecting a top and bottom flange with a solid vertical web.

gravity dam – constructed of masonry or concrete resisting the water pressure by its weight, but because of the greater mass of the material the downstream and upstream slopes can be quite steep. This form is suitable for narrower valleys with sound rock for a foundation.

groyne – a timber, steel or concrete wall built at right angles to the shore to prevent or reduce littoral drift.

historical periods:
> early medieval – A.D. 410 to 1066;
> medieval – 1066 to 1536
> post-medieval – 1537 to 1900
> modern – 1900 to present day

immersed tube – prefabricated units in steel or concrete laid in an excavated trench in a river bed, jointed and covered over to form a continuous tunnel.

impost – the top part of a pillar, column or wall which may be decorated or moulded and on which a vault or arch rests.

incrementally launched construction – a bridge is cast in short lengths on the bank and a section pushed out over the valley using hydraulic jacks. As one section is pushed out another is cast behind and stressed to the previous one before it itself is jacked outwards. Permanent and temporary support piers are constructed in advance in the valley. The process continues until the bridge deck is completed across the valley. The bridge is then finally stressed to its design load. Also used for steel bridges.

intrados – the inner curve of an arch, also known as the soffit.

keystone – the central voussoir, often decorated.

leading lights – two lights by which a vessel may be aligned for safe entry into a harbour, usually one inland at high level and one lower down.

lintel – a horizontal beam over an opening.

littoral drift – the movement of sand or shingle along a coastline by the action of tides striking the coast at an angle and scouring the beach material.

loads: dead load – the total weight of the bridge structure itself;
> **live load** – the weight of traffic crossing the bridge and loads from wind, snow etc.

locks: flash lock – a single gate in a river weir which can be opened to allow boats to pass through;
> **pound lock** – an enclosed chamber with gates at both ends for moving boats from a higher to a lower level and vice versa.

mass concrete – concrete without added steel reinforcement.

navigator or navvy – labourer employed to excavate a canal, later any general labourer.

oculus, oculi – a round window or opening.

O.D. – Ordnance Datum, the mean seal level at Newlyn, Cornwall, from which Ordnance Survey measures heights in Britain.

order – where bridges have two or more arch rings and one stands forward of the one below, the arch rings are said to be in one (or more) orders.

overshot wheel – a water wheel which is supplied by water at the highest point of the wheel and turns in the direction of the flow (see pitchback).

pavement – the main traffic-carrying structure of the road
> **flexible** – a pavement constructed of asphalt or tarmacadam, or stone or concrete blocks;
> **rigid** – a pavement of mass or reinforced concrete.

pediment – the triangular termination of the end of a building etc. over a portico. Similar to a gable but with a less acute angle at the top.

penstock – a valve controlling a flow of water in a large diameter pipe.

pierre perdue – quantities of stone tipped loose into water to find their own position and form a breakwater.

pitchback wheel – a water wheel fed at the top but turning in the opposite direction to the flow, more efficient than an overshot wheel (q.v.).

plate rail – a rail, usually 'L'-shaped, on which travelled flangeless-wheeled waggons of tramways and early railways, the vertical flange of the rail providing lateral guidance.

portal frame – a frame of two vertical members connected at the top by a horizontal member or two inclined members with rigid connections between them.

post mill – a windmill in which the whole of the upper part including the sails and machinery is housed in a timber building all of which rotates on a large vertical post to face the wind.

post-tensioned concrete – prestressed concrete in which the reinforcement is contained in ducts cast in the concrete and tensioned after the concrete has set by jacking the bars or cables against anchorages cast at each end of the concrete unit.

prestressed concrete – concrete containing steel bar or wire reinforcement that has been tensioned before the live load is imposed. By utilising the concrete more effectively than in conventional reinforced concrete, lighter member sections can be used for a given load, though the quality of materials and workmanship required is higher

reinforced concrete – concrete containing steel reinforcement, thus increasing its load-bearing capacity

rolling lift (Scherzer) – a type of bascule developed by William Scherzer in America in 1893. As well as lifting, it also rolls back at the pivot point. It had advantages over the standard bascule bridge as it allowed the bridge to span greater distances, providing greater clearance over the waterway when it was rolled back.

roll-on/roll-off ferry – A ship which is loaded and discharged by vehicles driving on and off via a ramp (abbrev. ro/ro).

side pond – a small reservoir at the side of a pound lock into which some of the lock water can be discharged or recovered to reduce water use at the lock.

side pound – a widened area on a canal, usually situated where the distance between successive locks is very short, in order to provide extra water storage space.

sluice – in dams a system to release water at times when the reservoir level is below the spillway so as to maintain flows in the river or stream below the dam site; in water courses a barrier that can be raised or lowered to control the flow in the channel.

smock mill – a windmill having a timber tower resting on a stone or brick base. The top of the tower (cap) containing the sails rotates.

spandrel – the triangular area between the arch and the deck of an arch bridge.

spillways – release water when the reservoirs are full.

squinch – a small arch formed across an angle of a building or bridge.

stanch, staunch – a flood gate or watertight barrier.

statute labour – the requirement of the 1555 Act for parishioners to work for a fixed number of days each year on road maintenance.

stench stack – a hollow column from the top of a sewer to some height above ground level to allow ventilation of the sewer.

stringcourse – a projecting course of masonry or brickwork, often framing an arch or below the parapet of a bridge.

summit canal – a canal which passes over high ground and falls in both directions from the summit.

suspension – in suspension bridges the deck is supported by hangers from a suspension cable supported by towers and anchored to a foundation behind them.

tarmacadam or tarmac – a mixture of stone and a binding and coating agent of tar for road surfacing, or of bitumen (bitmac).

tower mill – a windmill with a brick or stone tower. The top of the tower containing the sails rotates, the machinery in the tower remains stationary.

truss – a girder in which the web is formed of discrete vertical and/or inclined members. There are many different configurations.

tub boat – an unpowered canal boat of less than normal dimensions carrying a few tons; often towed in trains.

undershot wheel – a water wheel supplied with water at the bottom of the wheel.

valve tower – built into a dam or nearby for the stored water to be taken off into the distribution pipe network or aqueduct for transmission to the treatment plants.

voussoir – the individual shaped blocks forming the arch.

wallower – the main gear in a wind or water mill which converts the rotation in a vertical plane of the sail or wheel into rotation in a horizontal plane to drive the machinery.

windpump – a windmill where the machinery drives a scoop wheel or turbine to raise water.

wrought iron – an iron-carbon alloy with few impurities capable of being rolled or forged as plate or bar.

BIBLIOGRAPHY

Adamson, Simon, *Seaside Piers* (1977)

Albert, William, *The Turnpike Road System in England, 1663-1840* (1972)

Allen, Cecil J., *The Great Eastern Railway* (1956)

Barney, John, *The Norfolk Railway* (2007)

Barton, Barry, *Water Towers of Britain* (2003)

Booker, John, *Essex and the Industrial Revolution* (1974)

Boyes, John and Russell, Ronald, *The Canals of Eastern England* (1977)

Bressey, C.H., *British Bridges* (1933)

Chalklin, Christopher, *English Counties and Public Building, 1650-1830* (1998)

Cross-Rudkin, P.S.M. and Chrimes, M.M., *Biographical Dictionary of Civil Engineers of Great Britain and Ireland, Vol. 2, 1830-1890* (2007)

Denton, Tony and Leach, Nicholas, *Lighthouses of England and Wales* (2007)

Gordon, D.I., *A Regional History of the Railways of Great Britain, Vol. 5, the Eastern Counties* (1990)

Hague, Douglas B. and Christie, Rosemary, *Lighthouses: their architecture, history and archaeology* (1975)

Jackson, Gordon, *The History and Archaeology of Ports* (1983)

Jervoise, E., *Bridges of Mid- and Eastern England* (1932)

Moffat, Hugh, *East Anglia's First Railways* (1987)

Skempton, A.W., *Biographical Dictionary of Civil Engineers of Great Britain and Ireland, Vol. 1, 1500-1830* (2002)

Summers, Dorothy, *The Great Ouse* (1973)

Whishaw, Francis, *The Railways of Great Britain and Ireland* (1842, reprinted 1969)

Wren, Wilfrid J., *Ports of the Eastern Counties* (1976)